<u>Endorsements for *Enchanted Wellness - Ho*
ing it!</u>

"The power of Mind over Body was established over 75 years ago with the recognition of the *Placebo Effect*. Placebos reveal that a positive "belief" about the healing qualities of a drug or medical procedure can promote healing even if that drug turns out to be a sugar pill or the procedure a sham. The Placebo Effect demonstrates a direct influence of the mind's *positive thinking* on the biology of health.

Unfortunately, the public is generally unaware that negative thinking is equally powerful in shaping health. Called the *Nocebo Effect*, negative thinking works in the opposite direction of health and can create any disease and even lead to death.

The power of the mind is especially relevant in understanding the nature of *autoimmune diseases*, dysfunctions that are best described as "self-destruction." Multiple sclerosis (MS) is an example of an autoimmune disease in which the immune system attacks and destroys cells of the nervous system.

Diagnosed with MS, Jana Scholten's prognosis was that her disease would be a chronic life disability with no chance of recovery. Dissatisfied with the prognosis, Jana started her hero's journey by enrolling in Herbert Benson's Mind Body Institute, where she learned how "relaxation responses" play a major role in countering disease-provoking stress responses. Using relaxation techniques, in conjunction with visualization practices, goal setting and exercises in positive self-talk, Jana brought her body back into a balanced state of health and has been living a life free of MS.

In *Enchanted Wellness - How to go from hating disease to loving it,* Jana Scholten's personal healing journey encourages readers to shed their image of being helpless victims and learn how powerful they truly are. Weaving personal experiences with modern scientific research, Jana offers readers a valuable opportunity to become the master of their fate rather than the 'victim' of their life experiences.

Knowledge is power. The knowledge of "self" offered by Jana Scholten is profoundly "self-empowering." I highly recommend Jana Scholten's *Enchanted Wellness* as an empowering prescription for a positive, drug-free healing experience.

Bruce H. Lipton, Ph.D., stem cell biologist, epigenetic science pioneer, and author of the bestselling books, *The Biology of Belief*, *Spontaneous Evolution* (with Steve Bhaerman) and *The Honeymoon Effect*.

Jana's "Enchanted Wellness" journey covers the basics of healing, beginning with a profound mindset shift, triggering forgiveness with her important relationships, and lifestyle changes that enhanced her gut microbiome and body. And what an amazing story! I highly recommend reading her book to learn how you can love and kiss goodbye MS and any other autoimmune disease!

Dr Tom Acklin, former MS neurologist, Regenerative Neurologist MD.

"The book is an incredible read. I have seen up close the damage that multiple sclerosis can wreak on a person's life. It truly feels like a disease that will slowly consume your life. But while the author doesn't shy away from some of the more troubling aspects of the condition, this is a hopeful book that has plenty of useful information to make disease-free a reality. Even without the MS aspect, I found that there were some great anecdotes about dieting and recovering from mental trauma, which I shall certainly be applying to my own life!"

Peter Colley, Freelance Journalist and Ghost Writer

"Even with a number of years as an MS thriver under my belt, Jana's book showed me how much I have left to learn. Her personal story of trauma and triumph is inspiring, and steps are crystal clear with practical implementation. I was taking action before I finished reading!"

Rachael Naylor, MS Thriver, Voiceover artist, founder of The VoiceOver Network, presenter, motivational speaker

"Jana has led an incredible life, as any reader of this book will be aware. Her diagnosis of MS forced her to change her approach to every aspect of her life. The amazing result of her new mental attitude and healthier living was that she not only succeeded in getting rid of her MS, but she also improved many aspects of her overall life. This book is an emotional rollercoaster, full of stories that Jana tells with great passion and humor. Not only is Jana's story thoroughly inspiring, but her book is packed with helpful advice about how to lead a healthier life."

Stuart Pink - **Speaker, Coach, Educator at Brainarium**

"In this powerful and life-changing book documenting her own healing journey from MS, Jana Scholten comes to a profound realization that the quality of your life is determined by you and no one else. By coming to terms with the sources of her illness, she takes back control, using her own secret weapon: mindset. Through discovering the powerful connection between mind and body and then learning how to manage these through relaxation and visualization techniques, Jana begins to create her own movies in her mind, in which she stars as the healthy version of herself. As a result of this, her MS is now in a benign status, and Jana has decided to share her journey so that others can benefit from the lessons and processes she has adopted along the way. Enchanted Wellness deals not only with Jana's own healing but with the ability for us all to overcome physical, mental and emotional turmoil. And crucially, Jana shows the reader how the incredible power of love and forgiveness can be a catalyst for this healing. A very powerful and important book."

Damian Mark Smyth, multiple TEDx speaker and best-selling author on mindset and mental wellbeing

ENCHANTED
Wellness

HOW TO GO FROM HATING DISEASE TO LOVING IT!

JANA SCHOLTEN

This book is dedicated to....

This book is dedicated to all the entrepreneurial and supportive people who motivated me to share my story and write about my healing journey. Without the hundreds of you and your motivating words over the last decade, this book never would have come true.

To my parents, who did the best they could with what they knew and what they had in their life toolbox, provided me with moments of strength and incredible work ethic and gave me a love for the environment and mother nature.

To my big brother Carl who always provided me with support, love, and especially a laugh with beaming light and joy.

To my sister Mary who took care of me in my lowest point when I was sick with MS. For sticking with me despite my anger and stubbornness.

Who's now become one of my best friends and supporters in my life.

And especially to my gentle gent and husband, Daniel Junkins.

My best friend, my life partner, my love who has been by my side for better and for worse. May we continue on our joyous quest to live happily ever after!

Contents

FOREWORD

The first person I ever met with multiple sclerosis after my diagnosis was Jim. Jim was a happy man despite the lifelong physical challenges, and we bonded over a shared interest in spreading awareness of the illness and bringing attention to the *desperate* need for research investment necessary to find a cure. Shortly after we met, he insisted I join him at an "MS support group" meeting, something I thought could be beneficial at the time. My expectation was that I would meet people like me. People who were unwilling to give up. People who wanted to help each other live amazing lives despite the illness. Now, it's important to note that at the time, I was only 18, and I was then, as I am now, *determined* to fight the illness, remain positive and live a successful, full life. Therefore, I was fairly unprepared for the heaviness of the group as I stepped into an hour and a half of sadness, pain and victimhood.

I found that those in the group were not expressing their trauma in order to foster healing and resilience; instead, they were making a home in their suffering. And that is completely understandable. Many chronic illnesses, but *especially* MS, are shrouded in ambiguity. Moreover, whilst we've made incredible scientific advancements in our knowledge over the past 15 years, we still don't fully understand most factors of the illness. It is precisely this mystery that can make a living with the disease extremely psychologically tormenting.

The emotional dimensions and journeys of those living with chronic illness are rarely discussed. In fact, at the time of writing, research into psychological coping and resilience in chronic illness is still severely under-studied. It is through rising voices, bravely sharing anecdotal experiences that we learn to face the ambiguity and "shadows" of the chronic illness journey and find brightness in unlikely places. Voices like Jana's, who recounted her story with true sincerity and honesty, offer hope and enthusiasm to those who may be struggling with their own personal illness story.

At its core, Enchanted Wellness is a book about resilience. As someone with MS and an official MS Research Ambassador, I personally delighted in the mix of Jana's journey and practical life tips. Jana has proven herself to be a worthy role model, and her inspiring journey and commitment to living life to the fullest in spite of a diagnosis is nothing short of absolutely brilliant. She is a true disruptor of the chronic illness status quo, and it is a privilege to be included in a body of work that has all the inklings of a truly helpful book for both the newly diagnosed and those well into their health journey.

As you read this book, prepare yourself to be an active participant in the journey, not simply a passive viewer. Follow Jana's MS journey and allow yourself to reflect on your own as you do, whilst also lending your hand to Jana as she guides you, step by step, through exercises that endow a more positive psychological perspective on your chronic illness journey.

Mez Gallifuoco

MS Research Ambassador of Kiss Goodbye to MS, Mother, Innovator

INTRODUCTION

The idea of committing to a daily jog once felt like a different life for me.

There are so many tasks in our day-to-day life that we take for granted. The simple things like daily chores around the house, extra-curricular activities. All it takes is a few simple movements, and your body goes to work.

But there was a time when I didn't have any of that to look forward to, when I feared even the smallest movements would be out of my reach, when I felt like the only thing I had to look forward to in life was being a prisoner in my own body.

There is no known cure for multiple sclerosis. It is a progressive condition that targets the brain and the spinal cord, with the most common symptoms being muscle spasms, fatigue, visual impairment and mobility problems.

But my downward spiral didn't start with my MS diagnosis. It started long before when I was growing up and endured a difficult upbring amid sexual abuse and directionless life. The diagnosis just brought all these problems to the surface.

But today, I am MS free, drug-free, symptom-free and in benign status. Sometimes, I hesitate to say it out loud because I am shy by nature. But I have beaten the odds, living a fulfilling life with my husband Dan, have made peace with the ghosts of my past and given hope and inspiration to fellow MS thrivers. And when I go out for my daily jog, I always relish that rush of freedom and think back to the moments that catapulted me to this point.

Chapter 1

You Can't Take The Farm Out Of The Girl

ooking out her kitchen window, Bernice Scholten felt her blood rise to an instant boil, the words tumbling out of her mouth, "Oh no! The pigs are eating my tulips! Oh no! No!" It's a vivid memory of my mother, yelling at the pigs that had invaded her flower garden, bursting through the kitchen door into our backyard, flailing her arms up, down and sideways to shoo the pigs away, who munched on her tulip bulbs.

Everyone plans to leave home eventually, to forge their own path in the world. For the most part, this is out of a desire to achieve something for ourselves. But for some, the trappings of home can feel like a prison, reminding us of what we struggled through during childhood and the memories we want to leave behind.

That was certainly the case for me.

Farm life can be turbulent for anyone. The physical strain alone of tending to every little detail can take a lot out of you. But imagine having the added responsibility of living there. One thing I did like about growing up on a farm, though, was the fact that we could see the vast expanse of the world. We could see that the world was round. At the same time, we could see that it was flat. As absurd as it may seem, it made sense to us in the plains of Iowa. I would often sit in the hayloft, look out the window and observe miles ahead in those vast plains. No hills, no trees. Not a single thing was in the way of the scope of my sight. That was my escape. My escape was the hayloft, where I would sit beside that window and have access to the entire world right in front of me. All other troubles in my life dissolved. I could just focus all of my attention on the beauty of those plains. We called it the Haymow, but it was really the hayloft where we stored hay.

Iowa still had its downsides. One of the most difficult things that Iowans had to endure was extreme weather. It was brutally cold in the winter—as in negative 40 degrees Fahrenheit cold. Sometimes with wind chills, sometimes without them. There were no trees, no buildings, no hills around us, nothing behind us and not a thing in front of us to protect us from those freezing winds of the winter months. Instead, they blew right through us from whichever direction they came. I have vivid memories of storms, from winds to tornados, approaching from miles away while we watched in silence and awe. It was thrilling watching and experiencing the storms first-hand and being out in the middle of it all.

Summers were awfully humid and hot. Back then, we didn't have air conditioning, so Dad would blow one fan out one door and another fan out the other door. Then we would lie in bed until we sweat ourselves to sleep.

I considered the Haymow as an escape from a number of things. One of the main reasons I liked spending time there was because my parents often fought, which I hated. And I was afraid of my father's angry nature. So the Haymow was often my respite. Many times, I ran to the corn crib or the barn just to play with the cats. This was all I could do to steer away from my father yelling at me and pushing me to work harder. I escaped to avoid my father's constant bickering and fighting with Mom. I also wanted alone time away from them.

As a young girl, I asked for things and always received "No" for an answer. I asked for a horse, and my mother and father both refused. Another time, I wanted to play the trumpet, but—again— they refused. Instead, they tried to convince me to play the piano, but I was not the least bit interested. This kind of conflict was constant in our household. My father would then scream at me for something. I would then rush into the barn, sometimes in the middle of that harsh Iowan winter. In spite of the deadly cold weather, I would storm out the house anyways and into the barn until my mom would come out and beg me to come into the house. The cold affected me a little. I just wanted to put distance between my father and me. And this is what life was like growing up in Iowa with a father who was constantly angry.

The only real peace for me came from being in the barn on top of the hay bales and surrounded by all the farm cats. These farm cats were not cuddly house cats. They were wild feral, yet they were incredibly fun for me to tame. They were in constant motion, fighting, playing and always chasing something. But they kept their distance from me. Slowly and gradually gravitating towards me when I sat down in the hay bales, they always made sure to keep an invisible space between them and myself. The tenderness from their sharp glimmering eyes, the softness of their cheering meows, the lovely vibes of energy released from them, and the warmth of the piles of hay were my comfort. That was my slice of heaven, my escape.

I grew up on a farm near Sheldon, Iowa, the youngest of six siblings. Anyone who saw our family could have recognized that my parents decided to have their children in twos. I always felt that Mom and Dad had done this intentionally, almost like they had devised a strategy to make sure there were always two sets of hands for help on the farm. My older sister, Mary, and my oldest brother, Charlie, are about twenty years older than me, and my middle two siblings are roughly ten years older than me. Then came my brother Rich, who is one year older than me.

Mary had quite a bold character. She was unique and independent, for sure. She was one of the first people to open my eyes to a new food, and she was the reason we got our fair share of the inheritance. Having grown up during the women's liberation movement, she always sought fair treatment. Her presence always made my life interesting, and though we didn't always see eye to eye, looking back, I can say my life was all the better for having her in it.

Rich was the only sibling who was nearly my age. We were almost two years apart, so he was always around the house when I was growing up. I can't say that I liked him much because he always told me when we were children, even up to high school. So, I guess we were always at odds, somehow in competition with each other for our parents' attention. As we grew older, though, we became more mature and grew closer. We talk and see each other whenever we have the opportunity to, even with his busy life.

The creative one was Peter. He was innovative in getting out of going to church on Sunday nights. Going twice a day on Sunday was too much for him, so he always found a way to trick Dad into letting him skip Sunday nights. He once bribed Dad by making fudge and asking him to allow him to stay home. Surprisingly, my dad said, "Yes." That was cute. Aside from this and some vague memories of his hippie-like appearance and his quiet nature, I don't remember much about Peter's presence in our house while growing up, probably because he was over a decade older than me. Once he left for college, he moved out and visited just a few times, so I never got the opportunity to get to know him well.

Charlie was the eldest of all of us—twenty-two years older than me. Because of the big age difference between us, I considered him more like an uncle or a cousin than a brother. I never really got to know him because I was born when he was in college. I was only a toddler by the time he got married. I never got the opportunity to truly connect with him or get to know him as a brother. I couldn't attend his wedding because he got married in Germany and I was only a baby. Charlie rarely came home for visits, aside from the occasional family gatherings. Even in these family gatherings, I always saw him with the rest of my siblings, so it was hard to establish a close personal relationship with him.

My relationship with Dad was tense. He was a man of old-fashioned values, someone who believed everyone had their place in life, and God helped whoever said otherwise. I still have vivid memories of my alarm clock going off at 6 am and my dad yelling through the door, "You stupid, goddamn lazy kid; you'll never amount to anything, get the hell out of bed and get to work!" I would get up late just to spite him because it was my only way of fighting back.

A vivid memory I have was when I was three-years-old sitting on my mom's lap, chatting happily with her, when my dad rushed into the room, punched me in the face and gave me a bloody nose. From that moment on, being quiet was another way for me to try and avoid his unpredictability.

As I got older, Dad would have many more unpredictable moments where he would unleash his pent-up rage on me. I remember standing in the corner of the living room as he beat me over and over until mom got him to stop.

The harsh truth about cruelty is it isn't just limited to words and punches. Sometimes, cruelty is about hitting you where it hurts. And my God did Dad know how to hurt me.

When I was eleven, my dad gassed all my farm cats, beating them over the head with a sledgehammer when they didn't die immediately. I'll never forget that image of him killing the cats. After the incident, I took to calling him "Hitler," a moniker I kept up over the years.

Normally, when dealing with an abusive parent, the initial response is to put as much distance between you and them as possible. That wasn't an option for me. As I got older, my dad endured a few mishaps that damaged his health and made working on the farm even more difficult. He was electrocuted, had his leg partially eaten by a sow and had to endure a blood clot, which meant that my brother Rich and I had to take over more farm chores.

Dad had done and said all that he did as an attempt to motivate us to work harder, which wasn't a success. His anger and his cruel words were anything but motivating. Although he wasn't mean to me in the fields and for the rest of the day, I despised him for those mornings. I remained bitter towards him and everything he had done or said to me. I resisted being told what to do under any circumstance.

All kids grow up, losing their innocence along the way. But for me, innocence is something that should ebb away over time through a series of natural – and ultimately, fulfilling – experiences. But my innocence was snatched away at a very young age when I was sexually abused by an older relative at the age of five. In later years, I forgave my relative for all the abuse I endured and found a miraculous release of anger and upset and created a space of communicating with this relative that gave both of us a new sense of freedom and peace with what happened.

My relationship with my siblings was turbulent, partly because of the age gap. While most kids grow up in close proximity age-wise, I was separated by an entire generation from my siblings.

An early traumatic event occurred when I was four years old. I was playing outside near our house and next to our machine shed, where there was a dual tractor tire leaning against the shed. I was sitting inside the tire rim and playing/pretending to get my hair done (as a little girl trying to mimic her mom). My brother Rich wanted me to play with him in the sandbox, which was in a different area of the yard. I said, "No, I'm getting my hair done!" So, Rich jumped on top of the dual tractor tire and started rocking it back and forth. I stood up, and then the whole weight of the tire tipped over, burying my head into the ground. I blacked out. My older brother Matt saw the whole thing happen and immediately got my Mom. She ran out of the house. Miraculously, on her own, with no help, she lifted the 600-pound tire off my head. My mom drove me to the local hospital. My nose bled profusely the whole trip into the hospital. The hospital staff realized they couldn't take care of me. I was then airlifted by helicopter to the Sioux City hospital. While operating on me, they used no anesthesia or pain killers. I remember screaming the whole time. I vividly remember them removing both of my eyeballs to fix my nose. Both the pain and the experience were horrifying. Post-surgery, they had me in a bed that had bars on both sides, and I remember shaking on the bars screaming, wanting to get out. It felt like being in jail. The experience was seared into my memory with vivid detail. After this accident, I stopped playing with my brother Rich (two years older than me), and I had a basic mistrust of him almost my entire life (I did forgive him later in life).

I wanted to get out of my house as soon as I could. And as soon as I graduated, I knew I was going to get the hell out of there and never come back. Essentially, that's what ended up happening. Once I left, I only came back to visit my mother on certain occasions. I was not the only one who left. My siblings all left. Even though some of them claimed that they hadn't been abused by Dad, they left for good. They moved out pretty quickly and pretty far away, and rarely did they come back home to visit. This was a bit mysterious for me as a young girl, but growing up, I understood exactly what had happened. Unfortunately, for a significant portion of my life, I suffered from my father's verbal abuse, and I strongly despised him for it. It was only after years of therapy that my heart and mind started healing, and I eventually found a way to forgive him.

But even my attempts to forge meaningful relationships outside my family backfired considerably, and I have had two instances when I have been date-raped at the ages of fifteen and twenty-two.

Overall, my life growing up on the farm forced me to grow up much faster than I would have liked. I am glad that I took the time to get the hell out of dodge. I think I would have certainly gone mad if I had stayed there any longer. But the damage had already been done, and I was left wondering if I would carry those emotional scars for the rest of my life. Looking back, I can't help but wish I could have a redo of my childhood.

I thought that by moving away from Iowa, I would escape the trauma of my past and be able to be my own person without living in constant fear of judgment.

But the worst was yet to come.

Chapter 2

Growing Beyond The Trauma

I have previously spoken about how I was sexually assaulted by a relative of mine at the age of five. Looking back, I can recall the memory in detail and pinpoint all the moments it impacted my life (for the most part, this resulted in me gravitating towards abusive partners in relationships). But at the time, the memories were too painful to endure, too painful to even retain in my consciousness. This is why, somehow, I had completely suppressed such memories. It wasn't until I was in my early twenties that they were activated.

It happened during my first year at the Des Moines Community College. Sitting in sociology class one day, the professor was talking about incest. I suddenly came to the realization that I, myself, was a victim of incest—and a victim of sexual abuse. For some reason, though, I thought I was delusional. Later that night, I had a nightmare flashback of what happened to me when I was five years old. I remembered how the relative had assaulted me. I remember how traumatized I had been as a little girl and how scared I was that my parents would find out because I had thought that it was my fault.

To my utter shock and horror, these memories had been blocked to the point that I had started doubting my own judgments. "How could events of such significance be completely forgotten?" I thought to myself while trying to devise a convincible explanation. So, I sat and listened to my professor talk about incest, and the memories started emerging, one after another. I started having flashbacks until I thought I was going crazy. After the dreadful flashback, I became utterly shocked, and I cried hysterically. After that night, I had recurrent flashbacks of those memories. It was a traumatic experience; all of those previously suppressed memories suddenly emerging, and me not realizing I even possessed those memories or experienced such events. It was awfully traumatizing, and I truly thought I was losing my mind. So I—again—cried hysterically.

My roommate at the time, Cindy, was very concerned. So she inquired about why I was crying. Unable to discern by myself what was happening to me, I confided in my roommate. After describing to her the flashbacks, explaining my concerns, and all my doubts, she strongly suggested that I go to a therapist. Cindy reassured me that I was actually sane, that I was not losing my mind; those memories were real, she confirmed. I felt a bit uplifted; she was a nurse, so she possessed wide-open ears and a kind heart. I felt like she possessed a unique instinct that, when combined with her background, knowledge and education in the health sector, could not possibly drive her to make an incorrect judgment.

After our talk, I followed my roommate's advice and sought out professional counseling. Although I knew Cindy had my best interest in mind, I was still in denial that any of my flashbacks were real and that the entire experience had even taken place. I desperately needed professional reassurance that I was not actually losing my mind. In the meantime, the flashbacks and nightmares persisted, and they were certainly haunting me. After seeing a few different therapists, I found what I thought I had been looking for.

To my surprise, the psychologist assured me that I was completely sane. She confirmed that my flashbacks were true. According to the psychologist, the flashbacks were memories that had been repressed unconsciously due to their association with high levels of stress or trauma. The theory postulates that even though an individual cannot recall repressed memories, these memories still exist and may affect the individual at a subconscious level. After some time of being repressed within the subconscious, these memories can later emerge into consciousness. I was astonished that my brain could do such a thing. And this repressed-memory theory made perfect sense to me since I was so young when the event happened.

I realized that being aware of what happened and understanding all the details were not enough to make my memories or my anger or fear disappear, which made healing feel like an impossible dream. The memories were like an aged wound that had been freshly opened up, refusing to stay shut. So, I found a social worker with whom my therapy experience was quite powerful. And I quickly learned the difference between a psychologist and a social worker. Instead of just sitting there and talking about my problems, the social worker advised me to take action in order to resolve my problems. I needed to take action if I wanted to make any kind of progress or succeed in my healing process. The social worker was a wonderful person to talk to, keen on helping me attain an ultimate state of healing and peace of mind, and she was incredibly committed and persuasive. I knew I needed to take action to help myself heal; otherwise, I would continue to live in the horrific aftermath of the abuse.

The first action advised by the social worker was for me to confront my parents. Not only did I need to confront them, but I also needed to bring them into a therapy session for the confrontation. I knew that this was a vital step in the healing process, but that was definitely the last thing I wanted to do. I was confused, and I was terrified. For some reason, I believed that the entire ordeal had been my fault; I was sexually assaulted as a child, but it was my fault. So, I thought to myself, "If I bring my parents into therapy, they would perhaps blame me for everything, and I would lose their respect. They would think less of me."

So, I was not prepared emotionally. When my counselor suggested I bring my parents in, I panicked. I was embarrassed, and I was not ready for the confrontation and all the subsequent blame. Later, however, I somehow came back to my senses, and I realized how I had absurdly tried to reason my way out of the situation. Then, I managed to muster some courage to ask them to come in.

After driving four hours to the big city of Des Moines to come and see me and my therapist, my parents finally arrived, anxious, curious, and ready for some answers. I opened up to my parents and explained to them what had happened to me when I was a child. To my expectations, they were utterly shocked. They had no idea that anything had happened. They also never, ever uttered another word about it again, which only incited in me more feelings of anger and resentment towards them. Although they were well-aware of my suffering, they never opened up to me about it. They never tried to comfort me. I never heard those priceless and much-needed consoling words that anyone would expect to hear after having endured such a traumatizing experience as mine. I guess expressing their feelings or attempting to comfort me would have been a bit out of their comfort zone. After all, we grew up unable to express our feelings, never hearing from or telling our parents, "I love you." Although my parents' lack of empathy took a toll on me emotionally, I couldn't allow it to hinder my attempts at healing my old wounds. I had already started, and I had to continue.

Then came the second action: I needed to confront the relative. When the therapist said that I had to confront him about what happened, that I knew he had assaulted me, I didn't think I could possibly do it. I was terrified beyond belief as to how he would respond, how he would react. The therapist, however, was so adamant that she literally said, "You need to confront him, or you'll never get over this!". It had been years since I visited Iowa, so the two of us rarely saw each other. That year, I had planned on going home for Christmas, so I decided that was when I would meet him. That was when I was going to confront him. As uncomfortable as it was to even think about the confrontation, I knew that I needed to do it because of what the therapist said to me. And the therapist was always there to support me and to remind me of my objectives.

I trusted the therapist, and I agreed with her approach to establishing a healthy healing process. I needed to be honest with those who had been responsible for the damage. With Christmas fast approaching, I started rehearsing what I wanted to say. I was scared shitless.

Then Christmas came, and I was in Iowa. I was home for a short period of time, so I waited until the last days before my departure. Then, I finally did it. I met with my abuser, and I confronted him. "I know what happened when I was five years old. You assaulted me, and you forced me to do things I didn't want to do. I had unknowingly suppressed these memories until this past year when they were activated during a college course on incest within families."

"Wow," he said. "I had no idea you would remember what happened." To my surprise, he acknowledged he was to blame, and he apologized profusely. "I was in a drugged coma myself. I had to consume so many drugs at the time to escape all the abuse I was experiencing. I'm sorry. I'm really sorry I did that to you." He admitted that he had done it, but he did not remember much himself since he had been completely dazed out from all the drugs. At the time, he had a terrible drug addiction. I even remember once he tried to give me speed and marijuana when I was in third grade. He offered to help me in any way he could, telling me he would pay for my therapy and psychology books.

The confrontation was one of the hardest things I've ever had to go through. I was surprised and shocked at his response. And immensely relieved. I was grateful for the fact that he acknowledged the instance of abuse. After joining a sexual abuse group and hearing first-hand other sexual abuse victims talk about their horrible confrontations with their abusers, I was very grateful that I got such a supportive response from my abuser. I still felt bitter towards him. All of this wasn't enough to convince me the slightest bit that his actions were justifiable. The confrontation was the first step, and I had done that. Forgiveness was next, but that was not on my radar screen at that time. I didn't talk to him for the next fifteen years.

The relative admitted that he heard I had been going to therapy. Prior to my homecoming, Dad met the relative and told him that I was going to a psychiatrist and that I had "mental problems" because of what he had done to me. He yelled at him for what he had done. Dad thought I had gone crazy because I had dragged them to a psychologist. Going to such a professional in those days wasn't accepted, especially in my family. My dad was damaged by his brother's mental illness. My uncle had been in what people tended to call the "crazy institution" back then. My father became ultra-sensitive as a result of seeing his own brother become mentally ill. He was his closest brother, so his illness was extremely hard on my father, both emotionally and mentally. Apparently, Dad became a bit paranoid and thought I might end up going down the same path as my uncle: in a mental institution.

This experience with my father gave me a whole new appreciation for him. He had stuck up for me. He never stood up for me growing up, which, combined with his abuse, drove me to think he hated me. This rare instance in which he defended me showed he didn't hate me. In fact, he was concerned for my well-being. I was grateful to have found out what my father had done for me, and I gained a whole new perspective, a new light, on my dad's nature, who he was as a person, and our relationship. I held a fit of deep anger towards my father for mentally and physically abusing me and for having been so unkind to me. After this episode of him standing up for me, I grew a bit less resentful of my father, but the relative was another story.

Feeling bitter and angry for years after the confrontation, I blamed the relative for all my man-related troubles. Throughout most of my life, I was single. I could never figure out why I wasn't dating as often as most women my age were. Was it my appearance? I didn't think so. All of my friends had assured me I was pretty. In the rare instances in which I wasn't single, I experienced major intimacy problems. I never wanted to have sex—ever. I had mistaken this for being the product of a righteous upbringing within a Christian family where we were expected to abstain from having sex before marriage. Otherwise, we would end up in hellfire. Fundamentally, sex was wrong to just consider it in our community and family where I grew up.

To top it off, it seemed like I had a tendency to attract only abusive men in my life. I'd seen and experienced verbal abuse to multiple date rapes. In addition to being physically self-conscious of my body, I was terrified of sex, but I was clueless as to how I could deal with my fears. One of the first times I had sex with a man—without being forced or feeling pressured to do so—I completely left my body. I remember floating above my body, looking down at the whole experience as if I was a spectator. I was with a guy who wasn't some closet asshole but one of the sweetest guys I had ever known. So my mind, and my soul, had completely separated themselves from my body. After getting to know my boyfriend a bit more, I completely overcame my fears, and we had some of the best sex ever. What caused such a major change? Rather than being concerned about only gaining pleasure from the experience, he was gentle and understanding. He was more concerned about intimacy and constant communication with me.

Ready to move on, I relocated to Sioux City, Iowa, where I signed up for beauty school due to my belief that I wasn't smart enough for college.

I went to beauty school for a few reasons. Taking that option instead of the traditional college option angered my father. Once he heard about my decision, he was furious. He really wanted me to go to college. In seeing his reaction, I thought, "How can I go to college when every day of my life from the age of eight to eighteen you told me how stupid I was?" He had set his mind, and I had set mine. My father may have had a socially progressive attitude that his youngest daughter should go to college, but it had become almost a programmed reaction to resist him. He had also shown himself to be extremely sexist by showing his sons how to run a business and make money while never doing the same for me or my older sister Cheryl.

Aside from trying to get a rise out of my father, I also didn't know what else to do with my life because I had already believed I wasn't smart enough to make it to college. I had a depressing experience with a school counselor who told me I wasn't smart enough to go to college because my grades weren't good enough. But the truth was, I never really put too much effort into studying. I had been brought up on the belief that I wouldn't amount to anything. The only positive experiences I could draw on from my school years were sports, which sowed the seeds for my exercising regime.

I continued pursuing a career path in cosmetology for a while. I moved to Des Moines, Iowa, where I was a hair stylist and a manager of a salon for four years, and I was pretty good at what I did, so I was relatively successful. Yet, I was broke. I barely made $10,000 a year. I felt like I needed something to advance my knowledge and my career even further. I felt like I needed to pursue a more meaningful life. I managed to gain a sense of composure. After years of fogginess from the negativity implanted in my mind by my father, my mind started to clear. I considered going to college. Despite having put little to no effort into studying, I managed to succeed in college with a grade point average of 2.75. So I thought to myself, "I may not be so stupid after all."

But no amount of intelligence would ever prepare me for the diagnosis that would change my life forever.

CHAPTER 3

It Started With A Numb Toe

It was spring 1999. Something so innocuous, I didn't give it much thought at the time. Everyone gets a numb toe once in a while because they have been sitting in a dodgy position. We've all had that numb feeling in our feet and dismissed it without a second thought.

I had no idea that it would be the start of a life-defining illness.

It had begun after making the brave decision to turn my life around. I walked away from the life of hair styling and salon management, deciding it wasn't my passion, and I wanted an education. I moved to Cedar Falls, Iowa, to get my college degree in Public Relations and Spanish. After getting my double major, I moved to Chicago to live with my then-boyfriend.

One day, while working in my role at an insurance company, I noticed that my left pinky toe was numb. Long before the time when a numb appendage would send me into panic mode, my ideal solution was to buy a new pair of shoes.

But the numbness persisted like an itch in constant need of scratching. Gradually coming to the realization that this could be part of some bigger problem, I went to see a podiatrist who didn't give me any concrete answers. So, like most people wanting advice on the unfamiliar, I turned to the internet, but that didn't yield any answers either, with one suggesting that it may be down to a slipped disk in my back. Having never had a bad back before, I immediately dismissed this idea. I was hesitant to go and see another doctor and decided that it wasn't a big deal. The only action I took was to replace all my shoes. With the benefit of hindsight, I wish I had done more at that point. Then one day, I was in the gym, lifting weights with my roommate Lynne. And my vision started to blur. I tried to ignore it, but it increased every time I tried lifting weights. I took this as a sign that I had been working too hard and needed to stop. At the time, Lynne had a job in the healthcare sector, and after explaining to her what had happened, she insisted I go and see a doctor.

The fact that Lynne was so insistent on me seeing somebody overrode any doubts I had about seeing a professional. So I booked an appointment with my general physician, and they ran two separate tests for diabetes and exercise-induced hypertension, both of which came back negative. Yet, I was still referred to a neurologist. I knew I should have felt relieved at the negative test results, but the fact that they were referring me to a specialist told me that something was very, very wrong.

I began to feel the weight of loneliness crushing down on me, a feeling that was shared by my mother. My dad had passed away four years prior, and no one in our family lived close to her anymore. This meant that she had to deal with a diagnosis of onset diabetes by herself.

I could only imagine what was spiraling through her head after years of living in a house full of kids. Six children, the sound of voices, and everything else had just vanished into thin air. Everything had been transformed into a mere figment of imagination, almost like a hurricane or a tornado had come swirling counter-clockwise into her life, leaving her to recline in the aftermath of the storm. I started imagining how she was probably yearning to have us around her again, to fill her head with noise again and her heart with some kind of company. With children by her side, I thought, she would easily feel uplifted. To be honest, both my mother and father did not show affection or love. They had a stoic nature except in saying "No" to me and my older sister, Cheryl, to any self-interest in music or other things. There was little to no affection shown. Growing up in northwest Iowa was extremely difficult, and poverty was a condition that was known and feared by both my parents. Providing food, shelter and life's necessities were their top priorities. Showing love and affection was at the bottom of the list. But a softening of my anger and bitterness towards my mother began to show as my mother's health deteriorated. Unfortunately, her children were not by her side. She was lonelier now than she had ever been throughout her entire life, and I felt helpless. I could neither ease her suffering nor cure her loneliness.

It was during this worry for my mother that I had to comprehend my own state of loneliness. My then-fiancée revealed an abusive and vindictive streak, telling me that my legs were ugly and I should get a boob job, as well as assuming I should be his assistant in the future business he wanted to create. This gave me a less-than-pleasant preview of what married life would be like. I decided to cut my losses and leave him. It was difficult. I became unbearably lonely and wasn't sure what to do with myself. I was terrified about what the upcoming tests could mean. I think it was the lack of understanding over the disease that kicked my fear into overdrive. Shortly after I visited the University of Chicago hospital, a neurologist and his assistant ran a number of tests on me.

One week later, while I was at work, I received a phone call from the neurologist. In a concerned tone, he said, "Your brain waves are abnormal, and you should come back for more tests." I knew it. My previous concerns now seemed to be in the process of being validated. I had this strange yet instinctive feeling that something was going to be seriously wrong. With a wave of emotions rushing through me, I suddenly felt like my body, mind, and heart were at a standstill. It felt surreal as if I were daydreaming. Perhaps my mind was wandering off and playing tricks on my emotions, which happened to incite a number of physiological responses, some of which I had never experienced before in my life.

I had no idea how I could approach or process the information. Walking by, a co-worker instantly noticed the frozen tension in my face. "Are you okay? Is something wrong?" he asked.

I said, "This doctor just said my brain waves are abnormal."

He paused. Then he smiled and exclaimed, "I always knew there was something wrong with you!" Evidently, he found a bit of humor in the situation.

I laughed him off, but inside, I was shaking up.

I scheduled an appointment and went back in for the tests. The neurologist told me the procedures for the test would be quick and easy. "It should take no more than ten minutes," he promised. He informed me that the resident nurse and assistant would be administering a spinal tap. He then left the room.

I assumed it would be short, easy, and painless, so I settled into a more relaxed state. The resident nurse walked in with an assistant. She set up everything and brought out a needle that was over eight inches long. In an instant, my nerves now reached a near-boiling point. My eyes widened, and I began trembling from fear. Only one thought crossed my mind at that point: "Oh my God!" To get spinal fluid from my back, the nurse and assistant had me lie down. I rested on my side then felt an incredibly sharp stainless-steel stinger creating an agonizing rupture in my lumbar region. From the millisecond the needle came into contact with my skin to the instant the skin was punctured, to the bolting of the needle through my spine, I felt a stabbing, throbbing pain and horror. My hand enfolded the nurse's, and hers enfolded mine for support. The pain was so intense that I, unknowingly, nearly squeezed her hand right off of her arm. Tears and sweat were pouring down my face.

The first attempt was unsuccessful. The resident nurse tried once more. It didn't work. He tried again. And failed, again. It felt like he pierced through my spine over a dozen times, but—in all honesty—I cannot say for sure how many times he tried. I was in too much pain to even count. literally thought to myself, "I must not have any fluid in there!"

The neurologist finally came in. He ran to the nurse and put an end to what he was doing. He yelled, "You're doing it wrong, you idiot! Have her sit up! Not lie down!" Only a few seconds later, the nurse painlessly extracted the spinal fluid and was done with the procedure. The entire procedure took about thirty minutes. I was rattled and distressed on top of everything else that was happening in my life.

A few days later, I paid another visit to the doctor to discuss the test results. He informed me that my diagnosis might possibly be a disease known as multiple sclerosis, also widely known as MS. Though he seemed quite confident in the outcome of my test results, he couldn't diagnose me just yet. A definitive diagnosis would not be reached until I experienced symptoms, or what he called an "exacerbation." He was very matter-of-fact as he spoke to me. He had a horrible bedside manner. He showed no interest or compassion towards me.

The range of emotions and thoughts that rushed through my mind as he spoke were countless. I was dumbfounded and terrified to death. I was angry by both the news, the way he spoke to me, and because of how brutal he had been. I was confused because, at that time, I didn't quite understand what MS really was.

The conversation between me and the neurologist led me to a memory. I had participated in a city bike tour fundraiser a few years back to help raise money for MS. I remembered that at the end of the race, there were a number of people in wheelchairs. For most of these MS victims, frozen looks consumed their faces, and with bent arms and legs, they looked absolutely helpless. "That must be my future," I thought as I hopelessly went home and cried myself to sleep.

At this time in my life, my close friend and coworker, Tracy, invited me to participate with her in a class with a spiritual teacher. I took on the class during my time while waiting for a confirmed diagnosis of MS. During one class, she led everyone through meditation, the first time I had ever done that. During the meditation, I had a voice; a message came to me that I had MS but that I would be okay. With the drama of my mother's deteriorating health, breaking up with my fiance, my father having passed away, and unsure of what the future held, this message was just a fleeting moment in a sea of drama during this phase of my life.

I recalled the numbness and tingling in my toes—the experience I had attributed to poor shoe quality. Then I remembered the vision blurs that had given me a hard time just a while back. The idea of an official MS diagnosis started to feel much more real at this point.

Months went by, living in constant fear of waiting for the symptoms to catch up to the wheelchair reality I had glimpsed. And then I woke up one morning unable to feel the right side of my body. The entire half of my body was numb and tingly. Slowly, I crawled out of bed and into the bathroom, attempting to shower and get ready for work. But I couldn't shampoo my hair; I had no control over my right hand. Instantly, I knew what this probably meant, so I burst out crying. So gingerly, I crawled out of the shower and called my neurologist.

While sobbing, I described to him the details of my symptoms of tingling and numbness, and I explained to him how I was completely unable to use my right hand. He paused, then he burst out into an excited cry, "This is great news! This means we can now diagnose you with MS!" He was giddy with excitement, so much so that he was acting as I had just won some rare and valuable prize. Angry and pissed, I thought, "You asshole!"

The neurologist then told me to come in as soon as possible. I called in sick from work that day and went in. He explained to me in detail what MS was and the type of MS I had. It was called relapsing-remitting MS, a type of MS that progressively gets worse over time. Waving a light wand in front of me to examine my eyes, he continued, still in his aggravating mannerism and very matter-of-factly, "You will more than likely be disabled within ten years. Some major kind of disability will cripple you."

I gazed at him like a deer in the headlights. I thought, "I will be one of those people with MS in wheelchairs at the end of that bike ride. That is my future!" and again, my eyes burst into a stream of tears, feeling a mixture of fury, anguish, despair, and hopelessness. Dazed, the neurologist then suggested—in the most insensitive manner possible—that I start on a Prozac treatment to calm my nerves. By that point, I had just had enough. I could not handle listening to him anymore. I could not manage to conjure enough energy to respond to anything he said. I was done for the day. So, I left it at that and headed home.

I later learned that childhood trauma was significantly correlated with the probability of having MS as an adult. So I tracked back all my childhood experiences with trauma: the mental and physical abuse from my father, witnessing him gassing the farm cats, sexual abuse by a relative, my two date rapes and having the tractor tire fall on me with a traumatic surgery. When I was ten, I was involved in an accident with a Bronco truck. After the truck rolled into a ditch, I flew out of the window. I woke up from a concussion with the tire spinning by my head and glass stuck to my back. As a child, I also witnessed family members get into terrible accidents and become critically ill. I have to say, my experiences with trauma were countless. After discovering that trauma significantly affects the likelihood of getting an MS diagnosis, I can partly attribute my MS diagnosis to all these childhood traumas.

I knew that life presents curveballs, but this? This was more like a knuckleball that had smashed directly into my head. The process of absorbing the impact of the diagnosis and coming to a place of some kind of emotional and psychological stability and understanding would take more time than what I felt able to give.

Suddenly, something strange and unforeseen happened. Within weeks of my diagnosis, I got fired from my job. I tried to discern what happened, having been really successful in getting national media attention and receiving the "Employee of the Year" award. Now, I was being fired for missing a company meeting? I couldn't understand this. I had mentioned my condition to close friends at work. I was seriously concerned that this may have had something to do with the firing. I left, but I sued the company to make sure my work record was clean. Eventually, the company settled out of court with me and gave me a clean record.

I knew I had to make a dramatic move at this point. I became jobless. My mother's poor health was concerning, and I was absolutely frazzled regarding my diagnosis. I felt lonely, confused, and I was extremely concerned. I was near a breaking point, on the verge of despair. With all of the confusion and fear I was experiencing, I felt like I needed a radical change in my life. I needed to get away from everything

– from everything that had contributed to my escalating stress levels. So, I decided to take a major leap in my life and move to Colorado.

CHAPTER 4
From Lab Rat To Triathlete

One of my childhood dreams was to one day move to the Rocky Mountains, a dream that was realized when I landed what I thought would be an amazing new job as a communications manager in Denver. As soon as I moved to Colorado, I intentionally avoided saying anything about my MS diagnosis, doing my best to hide it from everyone, especially at work. At the time, I was participating in plenty of bike tours and other fundraising events for MS, which did not go unnoticed by my boss and co-workers. My boss, and my boss's boss, started making remarks about how I was doing quite a lot of fundraising for MS. Of course, I lied to them. I would simply respond by saying that I had a family member with MS, and that was the reason for my ensuing attempts to raise funds for its purpose. A part of me was also reluctant to accept that multiple sclerosis was a part of me, and at times, I felt as though not mentioning it put some distance between me and the disease. In hindsight, this wasn't one of my smarter choices.

But what motivated the need to distance myself from MS was the worry that I had been dismissed from my previous job because of my illness. Fortunately for me, I had a supportive network in the form of my boss and my assistant. However, owing to my previous success in getting hits such as Good Morning America, CBS Morning, and national press, my boss's boss had ridiculously high expectations for me and applied constant pressure to live up to those expectations.

If I hadn't been diagnosed with MS, I might have cared enough to try and live up to her expectations. I may have even set my own, perhaps even higher expectations. However, having been diagnosed with MS, I became extremely indifferent to anything but my own health and survival. I cared less about public relations or my status anymore. The public relations job was far from my passion at the time. I considered it as merely a job, a form of income, and a way to make a living—nothing more. Instead, my diagnosis, and consequently, my health, consumed my life entirely. They were my biggest concern.

While I was living in Colorado, I didn't experience any noticeable MS symptoms. I was actually able to take part in numerous fitness events. It didn't take long for me to start taking advantage of Colorado's beauty and geography. I participated in an Outward Bound hiking trip, which was a week-long trip. I also became involved in cycling, even taking part in the MS-150 Rocky Mountain Tour. Knowing that I was passionate about exercising, particularly out in the mountains, and knowing that I had been diagnosed with MS, my friend Rainey asked me to participate in this ride, "Well, Jana, you have MS, and you love being out in the mountains, so you might as well take part in this ride. It will help raise money for the MS Society."

My instant response was, "Okay, sure." Being from Iowa and having grown up in the middle of the flat plains, I could not help but be intimidated at the thought of exercising in the Rocky Mountains of Colorado. But I quickly overcame my own fears once the 10-year MS deadline struck a reminder in my head. Even though it was a 150-mile bike tour in the Rocky Mountains and I hadn't ridden my bike over 10 miles before, I thought to myself, "I have a "timeline! I will be paralyzed within the next 10 years." This reminder is what gave me the courage to go all out, with no doubts and no regrets.

What gave me an added boost of motivation and courage was the team of riders that Rainey had put together. Being part of a team was incredibly motivating. We often met at 7 am on the weekends to train and prepare for the big event. They helped me both physically and mentally. We trained in the mountains and in the foothills, and we trained as much and as hard as we possibly could. I was not experiencing symptoms at this point—aside from the numb pinky toe. Though I wasn't experiencing symptoms, as part of a clinical study I began participating in while living in Chicago, I was prescribed a drug, which I self-administered three times a week through needle shots. This also forced me to confront my deep fear of needles as well.

I was dead set on not allowing myself to become like the MS sufferers I had seen crippled in wheelchairs. My fear of being in a wheelchair and crippled by MS drove me to train hard. I worked myself into good enough shape to participate in the ride. We were in the Rocky Mountains, so it was a highly intense ride. Having trained for over six months, I felt great about everything, from my ability to go through with the ride to my overall health. I became extremely grateful for having found an experienced team to ride and train with. Riding a hundred fifty miles in the Rocky Mountains wasn't easy, but I loved the feeling of being fit and doing something so worthwhile. It was challenging, but it was invigorating and simply amazing. It made me extremely proud of myself, and it boosted my self-confidence.

One of the most difficult yet enjoyable and incredible experiences was Outward Bound. It was terrifying but incredibly rewarding. By far, hiking and cycling through the mountains were among the best experiences in my life. Living in Colorado and being a fitness enthusiast at the time, I climbed numerous 14,000-foot mountains. There were many weekend warriors who would compete against each other in mountain climbing. Being a weekend warrior, I was an extremely avid hiker and sportsperson overall. I climbed mountains whenever I had the chance.

The Colorado Mountains seemed to be limitless in what we were able to do in them. In addition to bike riding and mountain climbing, I finally learned how to ski in those Rocky Mountains. The Rocky Mountain skiing experience was priceless, mainly because of the beautiful snow that fell in Colorado. It wasn't hard frozen granular snow, and it wasn't mushy wet snow, both of which make skiing a lot tougher. The snow in Colorado was perfect, fluffy powder that makes the ultimate skiing experience.

Rainey then asked, "Well, how about doing a triathlon with me?" So I upped the ante by training for the Danskin Sprint Triathlon in Lake Washington in the Seattle area. These were smaller distances, more like beginner triathlons—roughly quarter-mile swims, 20-mile bike rides, and 3-mile runs. Although I lived in Colorado, I took part in the event in Seattle, Washington. Part of the reason the triathlon was unsuitable in Colorado was that Colorado has little open water. There were a few small lakes here and there, but nothing big enough for an organized race. As soon as my friend suggested we try the triathlon, I said, "Yeah, sure!" so enthusiastically and confidently that one would've thought I was a professional athlete. In reality, I didn't even know how to swim.

I grew up in Iowa, where there were more pigs than people. It's true. There are many pig swamps and very few lakes. I took a month of swim lessons to get ready. Eventually, I was able to do the dog paddle—not Olympic swimming, of course! And I did enter my first triathlon in Lake Washington. In that triathlon, I discovered that I had to overcome a deep fear of open water. As the gun was fired at the start of my first triathlon, I walked up to my knees in the lake, looked out over the water and was immediately overcome by the memory of my brother getting caught in an undertow on a beach when I was four years old. Frozen by the expanse of water and the memory of my brother almost drowning, I started hyperventilating. Luckily the organizers had these "angel" swimmers who offered encouragement and support to swimmers who needed extra help. An "angel" swimmer swam over to me and said, "I'm an Olympic swimmer. I can swim with you the whole way. If you get scared, you can grab onto this water worm here. We'll swim from paddle board to paddle board. Does that work for you?"

I felt totally taken care of at that moment and said, "Yeah! That works for me!" And I swam the whole way with her. She was amazing. I completed the entire swim. I overcame my fear of open water, completed the bike and the run, and completed my first triathlon. Even though I was one of the last to finish the triathlon, I took a lot of comfort in knowing that I had been able to finish it and had gained the courage to overcome my fears along the way. This first triathlon was the most amazing and worthwhile accomplishment so far. I gained more self-esteem and confidence and fell in love with the event. This amazing event was the start of a series of triathlons for me.

I was putting all my effort into my training and trying to throw off the effects of MS, but after a while, the MS started to push back. I would experience extreme fatigue after getting a full night of sleep and no exercise. I kept pushing through it by exercising because I knew it was good for the nervous system. In the back of my mind, however, I always held a lingering concern about the doctor's remarks. The lingering concern arose from the constant resonation of the neurologist's statement, "You will be disabled within ten years." Regardless of how hard I tried to disregard those words, regardless of how hard I tried to stay positive and hope for some kind of a miracle, I couldn't prevent my mind from imagining the bleakest episodes of my future with MS. I couldn't possibly just shrug off those disheartening and terrifying depictions of my future.

After my diagnosis back in Chicago, I chose to take part in a clinical study. Still going through a period of loneliness after breaking up with my fiancée, seeing a doctor gave me a sense of comfort, security, even hope. The clinical study aimed to compare the effect of two MS drugs, Rebif and Avonex, and I was assigned to Rebif. The drug's immediate side effects were so severe that they were almost unbearable. The protocol required me to self-administer a shot with a long needle several times a week, and after every shot, I woke up the next day with severe flu-like symptoms. I felt terrible the following morning and throughout most of the day, yet I forced myself to go to work and pretend like everything was okay.

Through all of those fitness activities, I was still part of the clinical trial. Knowing about all of my incredible fitness adventures, the doctors thought that the drug may have been responsible for my incredible abilities to still do such things despite the diagnosis. Ecstatic about the results, the company that made this drug then flew me out to Las Vegas so I could be a patient advocate for their drug. The all-expense-paid trip was incredible; it was a highly luxurious experience, and I felt amazing knowing that I was a healthy advocate for this MS drug. Obviously, they—as well as I—were mistaken when we thought that the drug was responsible for my healthy state.

Although I was taking part in all of these wonderful fitness activities, and despite having gained an amazing sense of joy and thrill out of them, I still felt a bit lonely in Denver. I only had a few close friends. One friend, in particular, Eric, was a saving grace. Although we respected and loved each other greatly, our relationship was only platonic, never romantic. I also felt like my job was grinding away, and I had taken a part-time job in retail because of the terrible pay. When the axe on the communication job finally came down (the 9/11 disaster occurred at that time), I decided to move to retail full-time, which proved to be just as soul-sucking, if not more so. And the pay didn't help. My rent was only $500 a month, but I still had trouble paying it. The only saving grace about this job was that I met many great outdoor enthusiasts and fitness buffs. In the meantime, I tried to look for another PR job but was unsuccessful. I had no money to manage, so my older brother was kind enough to loan me some money to help me get by.

The low-paying job made life quite challenging in Colorado. Sometimes, when biking outside of the city, my friends and I would get harassed by men driving pickup trucks throwing glass soda or beer bottles at us from their windows while we were cycling. While it didn't seem to be a serious threat, those bottles coming at full speed, at or above 60 miles an hour, could have actually done some pretty deadly damage.

After having already climbed several 14,000-foot mountains and after having enjoyed as many fitness adventures as I could, I started to really wonder about the social and cultural life in the Denver area. I had, at most, five close friends in all. And I hadn't had a date in over 2 years. All of these factors contributed to a quick change of heart. I started thinking of moving out of Denver to look for better career opportunities and a better life overall. Coincidentally, two close friends, Chris and Kathy, had lost their jobs in Denver as well. They were moving back east to where they were originally from—Philadelphia. They knew there were many more and better career opportunities in

Philadelphia. They asked me to come with them. I was a bit hesitant. But once they suggested I stay at my sister's house, who also lived in Philadelphia at the time, I became more interested.

It didn't take long for Chris, Kathy and I to decide to move to Philadelphia together. They were kind enough to move my things across the country from Denver to Philadelphia. As for me, I knew I needed to see my mother. On my way to Philadelphia, I decided to plan a trip to my mom's house, which would be the last time I ever saw my mom.

CHAPTER 5

Rock Bottom In Philadelphia

I moved to Philadelphia in the spring of 2002. Chris and Kathy were such a huge help in moving my stuff to my sister's place near Philadelphia. It didn't come to me as a surprise when they did that. They are big-hearted, kind, and generous. They were unemployed like me, and having grown up in the Philly area; they felt Philadelphia would provide all of us with more career opportunities.

Before I finalized my decision to move with my friends, I called my sister Mary to ask her if I could stay with her for a few months. Having been unemployed for quite some time, I needed somewhere to stay worry-free until I got back up on my feet. Luckily, Mary was very welcoming. I was taken a bit by surprise, and I felt fortunate at the same time. Growing up, Mary and I were not at all close to each other because our age difference was huge- she was nineteen years older than me! I accepted Chris and Kathy's offer and made the big move. While they drove my things to my sister's house, I decided to make the big drive later—alone—so I could see my mom. I stopped in Iowa and went to the nursing home where she had been staying.

During my short visit, I stayed at my mom's house. Staying there while she was away at a nursing home felt strange. She was not allowed to stay at her own house by herself. The first day was great, though I could sense how lonely she was. I could tell that she was not doing well. The second day, however, was radically different. On that second day, she didn't even recognize me. She couldn't even remember who I was. Dementia had kicked in. Her poor management of type 2 diabetes had caused numerous mini-strokes. I saw her deterioration. I had a terrible feeling about what was happening to her, and I could tell that she wouldn't be alive for much longer. I left and continued my road trip to Philadelphia. On my way there, I wept. I knew that I had just seen my mother alive for the last time.

That entire trip to my mother's was a key factor in my stress levels rising, and the higher stress levels were causing the MS symptoms to exacerbate. I was the baby of the family, and although I was a handful growing up, I was my mom's special child. Mom was my saving grace growing up. She was the angel because I could rely on her for a sense of security and safety versus my Hitler dad. Her life was coming to an end, and I couldn't handle losing her. I was too far away from her. I was unable to go home because I couldn't afford to do so. Mom finally passed away three months after my visit. And that was it: she was gone forever.

I moved in with my sister. And my MS symptoms became dramatically worse. All of the symptoms—severe dizziness, extreme fatigue, double vision, and a dragging left foot—had completely exhausted me. It was during my stay with Mary that I had my first major MS episode lasting for months. Dizzy with vertigo, I was bedridden. I was hesitant about seeing the doctors because I didn't have any health insurance. One day I got myself to the sofa, sat up, a major strain, and thought, "If this is what MS is like, I'd rather be dead."

Even though I was grateful to Mary for taking me in when I was at my lowest ebb, our relationship was not easy. For starters, there was a nineteen-year age gap separating us. And then there was my frustration with how she was treating our mother towards the end of her life.

Prior to living in Philadelphia, Mary had lived in Minneapolis, Minnesota, which was only a two-hour drive from my mother. Despite the fact that Mom was all alone, Mary never visited her. For this reason, I held terrible resentment towards Mary. With amazement and disgust, I often thought, "Gosh, she's right there, only two hours away, how could she have been so heartless?"

Being so close physically to Mom, Mary was the only one who could have comforted and accompanied her. I felt helpless at the time because I was a twelve-hour drive away, and my brother, Rich, was an eleven-hour drive away.

She did not help Mom, and she didn't seem to want to help her in any way. Because of her behavior, Mary appeared to hate Mom overall. Even when talking to her on the phone, Mary was rather harsh. Her harsh conduct with Mom ensued for years, even towards the end of Mom's life when her health had deteriorated. Mary knew Mom wasn't doing so well, yet she persisted in treating her badly and refused to visit her. The lack of compassion and empathy on Mary's part fueled my resentment even more. My anger accumulated because I had not seen, experienced or understood Mary's side of everything until many years later. I understood that Mary had seen Mom in a different light than I did. Being the baby of the family, I was somewhat spoiled by Mom. Even though she favored the boys in the family, she did treat me with lots of love compared to how she treated Mary.

Apparently, Mary also resented Mom for not having stood up to our father when we were growing up. Dad was an angry, upset and violent man, and no one had the courage to stand up to him, including myself. I was awfully scared to confront him myself, so I couldn't imagine how my mother could have. Dad wasn't just mentally abuse to me; he was also abusive to my mom, and our house resembled a warzone at times from all the bickering and screaming that had ensued between the two of them. Thinking back, I'm almost certain now that Dad had belittled Mom's confidence over the span of more than fifty years of marriage. Despite all this, Mary failed to show any empathy for Mom. And, for a long time, I failed to show any for Mary. I didn't find out until years later that Mary had stood up to Dad and Mom when she demanded Dad put his daughters (Mary and I) in the will with equal shares as the boys. Also, dad had thrown Mary across the kitchen in one of his rages. The drama and tension in the family home had far-reaching effects on everyone in the family.

When I actually felt okay and healthy, I felt I needed to pay my sister back for kindly taking me in. I sometimes cooked extravagant meals. I even tried to learn how to cook like Julia Childs. When I wasn't cooking, I tried my best to at least help out a bit around the house. When my MS symptoms kicked in, though, I could barely manage to get out of bed. I was bedridden for months.

Being almost completely crippled from the horrifying symptoms, I felt stifled and entirely helpless. Extreme fatigue overpowered my limbs, and my severe double vision often forced me to wear a patch over one eye. Oftentimes, due to extreme vertigo, I would have to hang on to walls or anything else I could grab while walking into or out of rooms. Eating became a nightmare. I was barely able to keep down anything I ate or drank from the severe dizziness.

Staying at my sister's house was scary. My MS symptoms became the worst I had ever experienced. I became completely hopeless. I could not bear the thought of living like that for the rest of my life. Severe depression consumed me. I felt my life bottoming out. Stress significantly worsened MS symptoms. I allowed my stress levels to reach their ultimate peak. My health sunk to rock bottom. My mom was gone. Flashbacks of my last moments with my mom, distress over my relationship with my sister, uncertainties with no job and alone added to my concerns of a bleak future for my health.

Just when I thought that my horrendous conditions could not get any worse, they did. I couldn't afford to go to the hospital. I couldn't afford medical help. So I was really, really at my wit's end. Fortunately, Philadelphia was where my best friends Chris and Kathy lived. Kathy and I would hang out and go for walks in the beautiful city whenever I was able. As one of the largest cities in the US, Philly was unique, where different cultures coexisted. Philly was also filled with trees, parks, other outdoor spaces and different unique areas. The city was so large, yet it contained many nature spots. The historical district was beautiful, and the city had amazing restaurants and bars. The only undesirable thing in Philadelphia was the weather. It was extremely hot and humid. I had experienced heat and humidity in Iowa during the summers, but Iowa humidity did not come close to the kind of extreme humidity in Philadelphia. I didn't know that such heat and humidity worsen MS symptoms since they cause inflammation.

When I first moved to Philadelphia, I didn't make many friends. I did start socializing soon after settling. I met a few people at a meditation center that was close to my sister's house. They put together group walking meditations, which I participated in whenever I could or when I had enough energy to go outside. Aside from these experiences, I didn't have many experiences in Philadelphia because of my health. Had I been to Philadelphia at a different time, I might have actually really enjoyed it, and I may have even gotten over the humidity.

Philadelphia was rock bottom for me. I needed to get out of my rut. Once again, I was at crossroads in my life, during a time when it felt like it was not possible to get it right. I needed to forge a new way forward for myself.

CHAPTER 6

Shipping Off To Boston

During my short stay in Philly, I managed to plan a short weekend trip to Boston and attend a networking meeting for jobseekers. I was so exhausted by the time I arrived at the meeting that I could barely gather enough energy for the network. So, I sat down in the conference room. While I sat there fatigued, disappointed, and rather hopeless, a man approached me and initiated small talk with me, introducing himself. After only a few minutes, I sensed a radical shift in my mood, mainly due to his humor. Those few moments with Ralph made the entire trip worthwhile, despite the fact that I was late for the meeting that I had come for. For years after this incident, Ralph and I became close friends and biking buddies. He even delivered the funniest speech at my wedding. My first encounter with Ralph at the Boston networking event turned my life around. At the time, I felt this amazing encounter was a sign—a sign for me that making a move to Boston would be a great decision.

Back in Philadelphia, I continued suffering immensely from MS. With no energy to work and extreme bouts of dizziness and vertigo, I felt I had a constant drinking buzz that wouldn't go away. I could not manage any kind of job, so I decided it was best to try contract or freelance work. I wouldn't have to commit to working anywhere long enough for others to know I was sick. My symptoms were horrible, but I mustered enough energy and courage to make a move to Boston. Since I was left with some inheritance from my parents, I was able to afford to move to Boston. I knew that was where I wanted to go, and I knew I wanted to live there permanently.

When I visited Boston to see friends, I fell in love with the old city. One reason I chose to move to Boston was because of its stellar health care. A second motivation was that New England was known to have plenty of colleges and universities, which I thought would be highly convenient for me in case I chose to pursue an advanced degree. Being an outdoors fanatic, I heard about the great outdoors opportunities in Boston for triathletes like myself. I was ecstatic about what awaited me, knowing that Boston was a diverse old city like Philadelphia. I could enjoy the outdoors but no longer at the expense of living in a land-locked state with not much open water. I had been looking for a place for my mind and heart to heal, and I found it.

As for Mary, I was grateful because she had kindly taken me in when I was at the lowest point in my life. Initially, I could not understand the relationship between Mom and Mary. Later, however, I under-stood that she felt a considerable amount of resentment towards our mother because of a number of different things that had happened to Mary growing up. Despite having gained a somewhat better under-standing of their relationship, I sensed my frustration was still there, but I also knew there was a lot more I didn't yet know or understand that became clearer years later. But our relationship had grown be-cause we had begun to know each other better. So there I was, leaving Mary and Philadelphia behind to move to a city I was fascinated by its endless opportunities and diverse outdoor life. I packed my things and headed to Boston, again with the help of Chris and Kathy. Kathy drove the moving truck to Boston with me because I was too fatigued to do it by myself.

During this period, I kept a journal of my thoughts. Looking back on it, I recall all the hopes and dreams I had for myself. I was in my early thirties and was considering the possibility of becoming a mother, even though the MS made me wonder how prepared I would actually be. The doctor had even told me that I could expect the symptoms to increase tenfold after having a baby. Of course, since I was currently single and not planning to find a new partner anytime soon, I figured I had plenty of time to think about how to factor kids into my life.

As a way of coping with my mom's passing, I brought a hanging basket of petunias to help remember her. During those times, when I was meditating, I found myself thinking about the idea of reincarnation; what could we possibly come back as. It comforted me to think of my mom flying around like a seagull. Spreading her wings and experiencing endless freedom to make up for the isolation she struggled with towards the end of her life.

But it also made me think about the idea of starting again, moving forward to something different... something better...

And so, I ventured onto the next, uncertain chapter of my life.

CHAPTER 7

Forgiveness Heals

I found an apartment with a woman who had a room for rent in Jamaica Plain, a neighborhood in the city of Boston. I moved in with her, and I started my life all over. Parentless at the age of thirty-one and no longer living with Mary, I felt extremely lonely. I knew I was ready to start over in New England, in the small city of Boston. It was beautiful, and it had everything I needed or could have asked for.

At the suggestion of a friend, I participated in The Landmark Forum in 2003, which was a three-day intensive course that sought to examine and challenge the ways in which we humans relate, communicate and interact with each other. The forum bases its teachings on what is referred to as transformative learning, which enables people to attain a critical awareness of themselves, examining the structures of who they are, how they think, what they know, and how they behave. In the process of examining and challenging themselves, people who take the course discover more powerful, clear, loving and impactful ways to communicate and cause powerful positive results in various areas of their lives: job performance, health, family relationships and basic human daily interactions.

As for me, I found a new, fresh freedom with my relationship to multiple sclerosis, and I began to feel and experience my body responding. The Landmark Forum and follow-up courses allowed me to be open to different healing modalities, providing me with an entirely new realm of understanding and recognition of myself. I also began having deeper, more personal conversations with my brothers and sisters that were more intimate, more forgiving, and more loving. A significant distinction that we learned was about truly accepting people for who they are rather than for who they aren't, essentially. We could choose to appreciate and love others for the times when they were caring and nice to us and the times in which they showed love and appreciation rather than hate them for the instances when they were unkind to us.

These conversations helped me attain awareness and gain a strong sense of who I was within my family and among my siblings. The conversations provided me with revelations and realizations about my relationship with my family members, which I needed badly at that point in my life. I needed to put my entire life into perspective, and I needed to find some kind of resolution to the conflict between me and the rest of my family. I knew that failing to resolve all the issues I had in my life at the time would prevent me from living a happy and ful-filling life. What I realized through the Landmark Forum was that the only way I could attain that resolution in my life would be to let go of any bitter grudges against or memories of those who were responsible for inflicting on me any kind of harm, whether physical or emotional. What I learned from the Landmark Forum and its subsequent sessions was to forgive my father for who he was, for who he wasn't, rather than lament over what or how he should have been.

As per the Landmark's teachings, I began the fundamental process of forgiveness. I started forgiving my father. And I started forgiving my sister and my mother. Then I initiated the process of forgiving the relative. As per the Landmark's teachings, I began searching for ways to love and appreciate them so I could finally attain peace of mind and happiness. Most of the time, my father had been excessively angry and mean, and his frequent verbal abuse was what had caused me so much pain and built-up of anger. I began recalling the numerous times when my dad was genuinely caring and loving. It was true that Dad had been verbally abusive, but deep down inside, he genuinely loved us. He genuinely loved me. On several occasions, I was able to recognize how much he really cared and loved me and how much he despised seeing me in pain. I recognized most of his pure intentions and his caring nature when he discovered the pain that the older relative had inflicted on me. When he discovered what had happened, I could see in his reaction that he truly loved me and cared for my well-being.

The same went for the relative who had sexually abused me. For so long, I had held a terribly bitter grudge towards him, but thanks to the Landmark Forum, I decided to let go. I knew that I needed to let go if I wanted to succeed in attaining peace of mind, and I knew that to be able to let go and attain peace of mind, I needed to find a way to appreciate and forgive the relative. It's true that he had assaulted me, which was beyond horrific and troubling. But did he mean to do it? No. In fact, he was not even mentally present when doing what he had done. Because of so much pain and trouble in his life at the time, he was on so many drugs that he was barely conscious. I later learned that over-consumption of drugs was his way of trying to thwart off so much suffering from the abuse that he had been experiencing. Consequently, he was unaware of his own actions. In putting everything into perspective this way and in setting aside the life-long grudge I had held towards the relative, I began to see things more clearly. Strangely, I actually felt strong empathy for the relative. I felt sorry because in being mentally and psychologically disturbed by the turmoil he had been enduring, he was suffering considerably. Having adopted the new mindset and new perspectives from the Landmark Forum, I decided the best thing for my own personal well-being and for my relationships was forgiveness. So I forgave the relative.

Prior to the forum, I hated him; I truly despised him for what he had done. I had been blaming him for all of my problems, for everything. That weekend of the Landmark Forum was a turning point; that's when I decided to forgive him after fifteen long, tedious, painful years. Aside from the rare family gatherings, I hadn't talked to him or seen him for that long. So what did I manage to do next? I called the relative, and for the second time in my life, I confronted him. Unlike the first confrontation, however, the aim of this one was to have peace with myself and with him. With all earnestness, I confessed to him that I had been doing him wrong by blaming him for all my troubles, then I expressed to him that I forgave him for what he had done to me as a child. Then, I cried some highly profound tears. He cried too, and that was the start of a fresh, healthy relationship with the relative. That was, however, just a start; after working on myself more and becoming more present and aware, my journey to forgiveness flourished even more

I also forgave my father. Dad wasn't alive, having died from the skin cancer melanoma when I was twenty-six, but I was able to write him letters and express all my feelings. I think back on Dad's own upbringing in which he had to endure a turbulent relationship with his own father and siblings. That, combined with the added pressure to maintain the family farm, must have worn away at him. Sometimes, I think about how events in my life panned out, and I wonder how my dad would react if he were alive to judge. We spent so many years being at loggerheads with each other. I wouldn't mind having a few of them back.

Essentially, I forgave him because he had done what he could and hadn't done what he couldn't do, and that was him. Whether I was happy with my father or not, I couldn't change anything. I could, however, accept him for who he was instead of being angry for who he wasn't. So I did. I accepted, and I forgave, and I grew more appreciative of the times he had cared and the times he had shown me that he loved me.

Next was my sister. Although I had seen and experienced a great deal of love from Mom, Mary apparently hadn't. I began to understand that her experiences with Mom resembled mine with Dad—the same experiences that had led to recurrent instances of distress, anxiety, stress, and reduced self-esteem. After understanding came forgiveness. It was only after really understanding Mary's rationale for having been so bitter with Mom that I was able to forgive her. I forgave her, and I was finally able to let go of my grudge against her for not having cared so much about Mom towards the end of Mom's life. Taking those courses with the Landmark Forum enabled me to finally let go of my grudges. After seeing how different people tend to react differently, I understood that Mary wanted my mom to stand up to my dad and to stand up for Cheryl. I finally saw where my sister was coming from. I was able to see this because I was also angry with Mom for not having stood up to Dad. And, I realized I had a different experience than

Mary – and that I could finally see Mary had her own way of dealing with Mom. I discovered a greater awareness of myself and was able to respect and see the viewpoint of others with respect and without judgment.

Once I was able to place myself in my sister's shoes, I began to understand her perspective. Similarly, once I placed myself in my mother's shoes, I was able to empathize with her. I realized that Mary wanted the best for Mom, but Mom's inability to put forth enough effort to attain what was best for her incited Mary's resentment. Once I understood Mary, I forgave her, even though I disagreed with her standpoint based on my understanding of my mother. I realize that my mom had done what she could to the best of her ability and to the best of her knowledge. Her inability to stand up to Dad did not denote a lack of wiliness to do so. Her inability to stand up to Dad was a reflection of her own instinct to just survive. Dad was, by nature, an upset and angry man, which was why Mom was just trying to survive versus confronting him by herself. With so many years of marriage with Dad, Mom's own world and culture may have turned her to just try and survive within the marriage.

Next was the rest of my family. Charlie was the eldest of all of us—twenty-two years older than me. Because of the big age difference between us, I considered him more like an uncle or a cousin than a brother. I never really got to know him because I was born when he was in college, and I was only a few years old by the time he got married. I never got the opportunity to truly connect with him. I couldn't even attend his wedding since he got married in Germany. Charlie rarely came home for visits, aside from the occasional family gatherings. Even in these family gatherings, I always saw him with the rest of my siblings, so it was hard to establish a close personal relationship with him, mainly due to the age difference.

Once I did my transformational work as an adult, I was keen on building a closer relationship with Charlie. But after he had explicitly stated that he wasn't interested in getting to know me, I was surprised, upset and truly hurt. Opening up and getting to know all of my siblings meant a great deal to me, especially after both of my parents passed away. I felt it was critical for me to take on getting to know everybody. And I've been going at it since. It has certainly been a slow process, but I have managed to create a few successful family reunions. A few years ago, we went to the Redwoods National Park in California as a family, where all of us met for the first time since our parents passed away. Getting together, putting aside all our differences, and just enjoying the rare quality time together was an incredibly worthwhile experience.

Since then, we have kept in contact with each other pretty well, and we even planned on doing something together again. But then the COVID-19 pandemic happened. With the pandemic came lockdowns, travel restrictions, social distancing rules, and other restrictions and protocols that have made it nearly impossible for all of us to get together again. In the meantime, I have taken up the role of the connector of the family. When Mom was alive, she was the connector. She had always tried to get us together for major holidays. After her death and after transforming my attitude and mindset, I've taken on that role. Depending on travel restrictions and how the pandemic evolves, I intend on planning more events for the upcoming year to strengthen our bond even more. In the meantime, I have been organizing video calls every now and then, especially for major holidays.

Not everyone shows up, so it's a work in progress, but I figured it's better than nothing.

I guess since Charlie and I were from different generations and had opinions and thinking from two different sides, he couldn't accept the thought of befriending me or allowing me to get closer to him. Whether we were on opposite sides or the same side never mattered much to me, but apparently, it mattered to him because he was harsh with me on more than one occasion. I once asked him for help since I was not doing so well financially. After losing the PR job in Colorado and working in retail full time, I was struggling to make ends meet. So when I turned to Charlie for help, he chose to criticize me for what he thought was poor money management. I was hurt because I felt like he was inconsiderate of the fact that I had been working full time at retail, which paid terribly. So, although he did end up giving me enough money from my parents' estate to pay rent, he had felt the need to criticize me in the process.

Since then, our relationship has been steadily evolving. Thanks to the Landmark Forum that I once took part in, I decided to make a radical shift in my life and my relationships. So, I've been gradually trying to get to know him and the rest of my family more, and I've been trying to mend any relationships that may have needed mending. In the process, I acquired a sense of appreciation and love for Charlie despite the fact that he had been so harsh with me at first. While trying to get to know him better, I learned that he had experienced some rough times in his younger years. Early in my parent's marriage, they were extremely poor, and there was a lot of worry about whether they could eat the next meal. Charlie heard and saw the concern on my father's face about the lack of money and security. That conversation with Charlie was a real eye-opener for me. For starters, I learned how he mastered money management. If anyone else grew up not knowing when your next meal would be or where it would come from, they would think twice before spending their money. And that's what Charlie did. Most importantly, though, I learned why he had been so direct with me for not managing my money well. I understood that he was concerned for my financial well-being. I saw him in a different light, and his concern for my finances was his own way of showing he cared.

If it wasn't for Landmark, I would have never come to these realizations. I would still be secluded from all of my siblings, and I wouldn't be able to see their side of things. Prior to Landmark, I didn't have the experience of "loving" relationships with my family relationships. Yes, it is true that I confronted my parents about my abusive relative, and I had stayed with Mary during my time in Philadelphia. But those were dramatic stress-filled moments in my life. For the most part, my life and my family life, in particular, were emotionally distant. My parents never told me they loved me, nor did my siblings and me. I knew I had family, but it mattered little to me whether I saw them or not and whether we were on good terms or not. The Landmark Forum opened my eyes to many things, one being the need for healthy relationships with my family members, regardless of how much I may have thought that I didn't need them. I realized I had a family that, for decades, I had no idea who they were. I realized that all of our differences needed to be placed aside for the sake of our relationship.

Yes, life is a work in progress for everyone. Geographically, we are widely dispersed throughout different regions in the US. Not one of us lives in Iowa! That should tell you a lot right there. Politically, we have all taken different sides, and in terms of religion, we all hold different beliefs. I'm sure that's typical of many families. Each one of us experienced our parents differently. My father exhibited an abusive nature towards some of us more than others. In addition, the culture we were brought up in was emotionally distant. This correlates with my mother and father's upbringing in their own families. My parents were simply surviving and trying to make ends meet.

Our lives were consumed with working hard just to survive. Loving relationships and fond memories were low on the priority list with our parents.

Of course, this is understandable considering how the boys were always treated better than us two girls in my viewpoint anyway. The boys were allowed to do more farm work where as my sister and I did housework and weren't paid for it as the boys were paid for all the work they did. I can understand how they would disagree on having been abused in any way. My sister, however, agrees that she was verbally and physically abused by dad. As mentioned earlier, both Mary and I were left out of the will until Mary threatened to disown the entire family if we were not included equally in the will. And the fact that our mother never stood up for either girl in the family shows how deep the sexism ran in the family. Growing up as a female in our household was tough, but growing up with my dad as a father was mentally and psychologically exhausting. I still can't figure out why my parents never expressed their affection or love for us. Not once did they say, "I love you." Not once did they say "Good job," and hugging, as well as all other forms of affection or encouragement, were practically out of their realm of possibility. Somehow, I think if the boys were asked about the casual sexism in our family, we'd be having a different conversation. But these minor differences between us made it almost impossible for us to fully embrace each other despite the fact that we are all mature adults.

Sometimes my efforts seem so futile that I feel like simply giving up. I have been having conversations with all five of them, but when it gets tough at times, I nearly regret having gotten myself into all this Landmark work in the first place. But then I come back to my senses and push further for stronger bonds both because I love them and because the only way I can move towards a positive future is if I am not weighed down by the wounds of the past.

Today, I'm grateful for having worked on my relationships with my siblings. I have come to love and appreciate every single one of them for who they are and who they aren't. I appreciate and love them regardless of their flaws, my flaws or any differences between us. I've realized that family will always be there. And that we really do need each other whether we realize it or not

The Landmark Forum was a turning point in my life, teaching me about the miraculous healing power of forgiveness, specifically, those who had caused me the most pain and suffering in my life. I began to experience noticeable changes in my health state, realizing how much damage can be caused by suppressed anger. The anger that I had held within me was consuming my physical health, but once I forgave, the anger became an erupting mass, being released out of my body along with the toxicity with which it entered. I noticed the more work I did, the better I felt physically and emotionally. I also realized that I had been blinded by my grudges, my bitterness towards my family members, and my relentless and constant blaming of my older relative and my father for my problems. Thanks to the courses and the forum, I came to the realization that families are not—and never will be— perfect, yet they will always be there, whether we want them or not, whether I want them or not.

Forgiveness truly heals after gaining a sense of gratitude for having come to my senses and for forgiving my family. I was finally able to love them again, and—after decades—I was finally able to move on and live with peace of mind. After decades, I was finally able to break the vicious cycle that I had trapped myself in. I finally broke the cycle of attracting only men who were abusive to me. Consequently, I found someone who was different, someone who later turned out to be the love of my life. Forgiveness is profound. It was profound for me, for my body, my relationships, my love life, and my physical and mental health. So my last step in the forgiveness-healing process was to forgive myself, and that's what I did. And I forgave MS.

CHAPTER 8

The Mind / Body Connection

After reaping the emotional and physical catharsis granted by the Landmark Forum, I decided to continue with it. So, I took part in a year-long program at Landmark Education. In the spring of 2005, towards the end of the course, I woke up one Saturday morning fully energized, planning to go for a run. But as I swung my feet off the bed, I leaned over, and at that moment, I experienced an intense and terrible sense of vertigo. The next thing I knew, I was lying on the ground. Unable to stand on my feet again, I slowly and carefully crawled my way back to the bed. The entire room was spinning endlessly, so all I could do was lay back and wait out vertigo, convinced that the day was now ruined and unsalvageable. I canceled my jog as well as the seminar that I was supposed to take part in. There was absolutely no way I could balance myself on my own feet, let alone make the daily jog.

I cried hysterically, pushed to my breaking point. It had been years since I had an MS attack. I thought to myself, "How could this happen now? I've been doing so well." I picked up the phone and called my friend and mentor David for some advice. After explaining to him what had happened, he asked, "Do you know that each time you have an attack, you are always the one having the attack?"

I was devastated by what David – one of my most trusted confidantes – was saying to me. I protested, "There's nothing I can do! I have nothing to do with MS or any of its symptoms. It just happens to me, and I have no control over it! I'm only a victim!" I tried to explain.

Then, he tried to clarify for me what he meant, "Well, I'd like you to just consider that you might have some control over what happens or may happen to you. You may want to consider that the quality of your life is determined by you and no one else. Just consider that. I'm not blaming or anything like that, but I think you should just consider it as like an opportunity to see life from a different angle, to take an active viewpoint, to own your life." At this point, I was very tired, so after telling him that I would consider what he had said, I ended the conversation. At that time, I only thought over his words for about a few more seconds before I crawled back to bed, too exhausted to give his words any more thought. The day had barely started, and I already felt like I was completely drained.

When I woke up later, I was absolutely stunned to find that the attack had stopped and the vertigo was gone. A typical MS attack usually lasts for weeks or even months at a time. That morning's attack, however, had been so short; it lasted for only a few hours. It was remarkable, absolutely unbelievable. After that initial shock subsided, I pulled myself together and started pondering what had happened. I tried to make some sense of what had taken place. What was different about this incident? Why was this MS attack different? Why was it so much shorter? What had I done differently? Were my own actions and thoughts possibly responsible for the shift in my body's physiological response? I was determined to get to the bottom of this breakthrough and whether I could replicate it in the face of another attack.

After tracing back all of what had happened that morning, I recalled David's advice. He had insisted that I would be able to take control of the illness. He insisted that's what I should do rather than allowing it to take control over me. David had been certain that I could turn my life around with one secret weapon: my mind. Although I had been so tired after our conversation, I did reflect on his advice. I considered the possibility of using my own mind and thoughts to heal myself.

Thinking over all of what had happened, I asked myself, "Could this have had anything to do with this wonderful surprise? Could my own thoughts have had anything to do with the incredibly short episode of MS attack that I had just experienced?

Once I posed myself these initial questions, I couldn't help but start to believe a bit more that a true, perhaps miraculous connection exists between one's mind and body. I thought, "Wow. Amazing! Maybe there is something to this mind-body connection stuff. If this is what happened to me, then it really does work."

My friend David had not mentioned anything to me about mind-body work or anything explicitly in connection with it. Yet, it was the first thing that came to my mind in recalling David's advice. Three years earlier, when I was living in Philadelphia with my sister, I visited Boston. At that time, Amanda, a close friend of mine, lived in Boston, and she mentioned that I ought to look into Herbert Benson's Mind Body Institute. I didn't give Amanda's words much thought— until that particular morning when I woke up to find that my MS symptoms had vanished. Flashbacks of my discussion with Amanda gradually started making their way back into my memory, and as I recalled more of her advice, I became increasingly content that I needed to try mind-body medicine. After that morning's incident, and after the recollection of my conversations with David and Amanda, I was convinced that they were onto something. I refused to put it down to coincidence, convinced that my mind and body were truly connected. I had a strong instinctive feeling that my mind significantly contributed to my body's response to MS that morning, so I set out to prove myself right.

Soon after my short MS attack, I enrolled in Herbert Benson's Mind-Body Institute program. Back when Benson was a young cardiologist in Boston, he noticed a trend among his patients with high blood pressure or hypertension, a precursor to heart disease. Once he prescribed medications to these patients, he noticed they often complained about fainting or dizziness. These were side effects of lowered blood pressure from the medications. Patients went from feeling fine to being burdened with irritating and disabling side effects, all as a result of the medicine he prescribed— this troubled Dr Benson. After a while, he noticed that this phenomenon was quite common, not only among his own patients but also among others.

Most people are aware that individuals' blood pressure, when measured in the doctor's office, is often significantly higher than when measured by the patients themselves at home or in other settings. Dr Benson began to speculate that patients experienced an increase in blood pressure because they were nervous, so he supposed that blood pressure levels were significantly correlated with stress levels. Today, this seems to be an obvious association, but when Dr Benson came up with such speculations, no one in the medicinal field had ever explored the relationship between stress and blood pressure levels even though high blood pressure was known to be a major contributor to heart attacks. Such speculations sparked a unique interest in Dr Benson, which led him to investigate more in-depth the relationship between the mind and body.

Dr Benson decided to make a big change in order to find some answers. He stopped his clinical work and, instead, became a research fellow at the Harvard Medical School in the physiology department. As a researcher, Benson delved deep into this relationship between the mind and body, asserting that the mind and body were two parts of the same system, a connection that people seldom recognize. This was when he introduced what he called the relaxation response, which is a more technical and scientific term for meditation and the kind of effect it can have on the body. Once an individual relaxes or meditates, the body typically responds according to that relaxed state. According to Benson, the body's physiological response is usually in the form of reduced stress levels, which is likely to cause a change in other physiological responses, such as reduced heart rate or blood pressure. Accordingly, the relaxation response activates a part of the body's nervous system known as the parasympathetic nervous system. This part of the nervous system enables the body to heal and rejuvenate itself. Most importantly, it enables the body's immune system to work more efficiently. The parasympathetic nervous system is active when we are in our most relaxed states, like when we are sleeping, meditating, praying, listening to calming music, or doing repetitive physical or mental actions over long periods of time.

About half a century before Dr Benson, the fight-or-flight response, or sympathetic nervous system, was discovered. Unlike the parasympathetic nervous system, which is activated upon relaxation, the sympathetic nervous system elicits a sort of survival response in our bodies when the mind interprets stressful situations as being imminent. Heart rate, blood flow to the muscles, breathing rate and metabolic rate, are heightened with a release of hormones throughout the body. Anxiety and tension are often considered as triggers of the fight-or-flight response in situations where there is a perceived threat that does not actually exist. The problem lies in the long-term effects of stress and anxiety. When an individual is frequently exposed to stressful situations, long-term accumulation of the body's fight-or-flight response to these frequently perceived threats may eventually cause breakdowns in multiple bodily functions or systems. So, in today's fast-paced world where most people are in constant, relentless pursuit of more success, higher education, happier lives, better relationships, and more, exposure to more stressful or anxiety-provoking situations is not uncommon. This means, overall, our sympathetic nervous system is probably being activated more frequently. It's no surprise, then, that more people are suffering from anxiety or stress-related illnesses today than ever before.

Dr Benson discovered there were two essential elements for activating the relaxation response. The first element is a mental device to focus on, which can be as simple as a sound, word or phrase or a fixed gaze at an object. The second element is a passive attitude, which means that an individual shifts their focus away from how well he or she is concentrating and instead allows thoughts to simply pass by and continue back to their mind's focus. When I exercise over long distances or over a long time, I can honestly say this has happened to me sometimes. I begin to operate in what is sometimes called "the Zone," where time and space are non-existent and running or biking itself becomes nearly effortless. For the relaxation response to be triggered, an individual can perform any simple act so long they remain focused on one thing. Several religions include rituals or practices in which their believers carry out practices that elicit the relaxation response— usually in the form of prayers. These religious practices have proven effective for those who follow them. Individuals who do not associate themselves with any particular religious belief have found other effective ways for inducing the relaxation response. Yoga, walking, swimming, knitting and many other simple practices carry the potential to activate the same relaxation response. Taking on these kinds of relaxation techniques and practices and utilizing them effectively can help bring the body back to a balanced state. In attaining a healthy balance between being stressed and being in a relaxed state, an individual lessens the impact or damage caused by the fight-or-flight mode, thus contributing to an improvement in overall health.

I took on Herb Benson's program, wherein numerous therapists and other specialists were asked to come in and talk. One therapist, in particular, attracted my attention. When I sat down and talked to her, she explained to me how she had recommended visualization as a healing technique for cancer patients who were seeing amazing results.

When I asked her if the program helped people with multiple sclerosis, she replied, "Of course! I've had a number of cancer patients heal themselves completely. You can too." Then, she mentioned how some cancer patients had significantly reduced their tumors, and others had even destroyed tumors up to the size of a baseball. They showed up to their chemo surgery only to find that their tumors had disappeared. The surgeons were astonished.

Her words of encouragement instantly sparked my attention and ignited a new sense of hope, inspiring me to take on visualization myself and discover my own techniques. Visualization techniques were designed for people to see themselves succeeding with their health and resolving issues or concerns by visualizing themselves healthy and well. These techniques were similar, or even the same as visualization techniques many high performing Olympic athletes, entertainers, and entrepreneurs have been using for the previous forty years: Muhammad Ali, Jim Carrey, Al Geiberger and Tiger Woods all famously saw their goals achieved years before they arrived. Scott Adams, the creator of the Dilbert cartoon, reportedly visualized his dreams and wrote it down fifteen times in a row every day, and within a matter of months, his goals had been reached. There are theories as to how it works. By being able to paint a concrete picture of what success looks like, it becomes less abstract and more obtainable. In reminding one's self every day of what their true goals are, they focus more on the things they really want to achieve. When they know what they're looking for, their brain is programmed to be more receptive to possible opportunities that are aligned with their goal. Though it may feel a bit strange at first, there are multiple ways through which one can start visualizing their goal. I practiced the following visualization techniques, which may also help anyone else taking on visualization:

Write down goals on paper by hand

In writing down goals by hand as opposed to a phone or laptop, they are more easily internalized at a subconscious level. Those who feel intimidated by the idea of trying to conjure up a picture-perfect image of what success means to them may want to consider putting pen to paper to figure out what they want in life. There is some effectiveness in being able to synthesize all your goals into a few words. By setting a constant reminder for yourself of what you hope to accomplish most and routinely engaging with your goals, the rest (including the necessary hard work) can fall into place. And by being able to communicate your goals with words, you can more easily imagine them for some on-the-go inspiration. At the same time, written goals should be concrete and specific. Failing to pinpoint exactly what it is you want or need to accomplish will make it hard to achieve.

Talk to yourself. Talk positively.

I bet everyone has noticed how young toddlers and children talk to themselves often. Before children even have the faculties to talk to others, they talk to themselves. In their private dialogue, they make sense of the world and form thoughts for themselves. When they have developed sufficient language skills, that's when they can fully direct their thoughts outwards—perhaps to their parents, family members, themselves, friends, or even with imaginary friends. The benefits of self-talk or intrapersonal communication, however, aren't limited to children only. Self-talk has been found to benefit adults just as much as children. Private speech, or talking to one's self, can be done for several purposes. It can be done to give oneself an internal pep-talk, to analyze past events, to weigh both sides of a decision, to release pent-up stress or aggression, to rehearse important conversations, to practice important speeches and presentations, or to fantasize about a great and promising future. Sometimes, the most effective self-talk is done in front of the mirror and with eye contact.

Forms of inspirational private speech can include planning out an acceptance speech for a big award, imagining a big presentation, re-hearsing a conversation with your biggest role model, and anticipating questions that the media might ask about the release of your book. By allowing yourself to get carried away with self-talk, you're pepping up. You're getting motivated. You're seeing yourself through a very logical (and therefore, less overwhelming) aspect of your future success. On the other hand, negative self-talk could lead to you discouraging or scaring yourself out of taking a certain course of action or choice or simply causing yourself to become indifferent towards what you would otherwise find interesting. Those who realize the path of negativity into which they've become absorbed may often feel the need to tell themselves to shut up out loud to stop their own negative narrative from controlling their thoughts and lives.

So, positive affirmations are essential for effective self-talk. If you're trying to heal, consistently aim to convince yourself that you are and you will be healed. Aim to remind yourself that you love yourself just the way you are!

Imagine your goals from your personal perspective

For some people, imagining future success is easy. It's something to occupy your mind on the daily commute, in the shower, before falling asleep, procrastinating from work, and otherwise killing time. It's like shooting a movie in your head, only less expensive. But in the movie of your life, remember that you are the actor, the director, and the writer - the camera should be adjusted to your perspective. So don't imagine Reese Witherspoon or George Clooney as the leading actor. Imagine *you* — and try to imagine the camera going through the movie from the first-person perspective, starting from where you want to start and ending when you're happiest. By seeing the world through your successful lens, you can best anticipate the steps it will take to get to where you want to be, and you can make the actual event more accessible to you. Most important to the successful pursuit and attainment of goals is the absence of fear. Fear in all forms—particularly fear of failure—can set you up for the very thing you fear. Fear of failure, for instance, is likely to impede any intentions of or attempts at self-development, progress, or positive change.

Add in as many details as possible

When you are accepting a best humanitarian award, what shoes are you wearing? Who is in the stands, watching your shining moment from ten feet away? Are you trembling, or are you brimming with confidence? These details are what make such moments of glory worth savoring— even if they are all just in your head. By polishing the small stuff, you can deepen the richness of your Big Picture.

Visualize goals

A major factor contributing to success in the attainment of goals is visualization. Make sure that every goal includes a viable outcome. Focus on the value you are providing for others if you're a business. Visualize success. By constructing a visual of what you're getting yourself into in order to reach your ultimate goal or simply by setting milestones for yourself and seeing them pass in vivid detail in your mind's eye, you are setting yourself up, brick by brick, for ultimate victory. Of course, visualization itself is insufficient to turn dreams into reality. It is insufficient since visualization itself doesn't work miracles. The most vital element for the attainment of any goal is action. To turn any dreams into a reality, one has to actually take action. You have to take action and take all the necessary steps along the way to turn any dreams into a reality. You can't just dream; you have to do the work to make your dream work.

As for me, I took on the visualization every single night. I visualized the size and shape of the lesions in my brain. Then I visualized them shrinking and shifting colors to an almost gold. Then I visualized them vanishing. If you could wave a magic wand and get the result you want, what would that be? Here's a great visualization success example: https://www.youtube.com/watch?v=DfLLNksZmoY

Billy Mills, 10000 Meter Gold Medal

Thoughts Inquiry

I also noticed I could control symptoms if they showed. I got to a point when every time I experienced an MS attack or MS symptoms, I would do some self-talk in which I questioned myself a series of five questions:

- Who am I being right now?

- What am I saying to myself?

- Are those thoughts true? (usually, the answer is "No")

- What can I create as a way of being for myself?

- Who can I be? Can I be vibrant and joyful!? Perhaps I can be loving and free! I will also be healthy and grateful!

After several times of following these visualization techniques, I eventually got to a point where I could make the MS symptom go away immediately. After several successful attempts, I knew I was finally getting myself into something worthwhile. I knew that a lot of positive outcomes awaited me as long as I continued to practice it consistently. I invite you to go through an inquiry with yourself using this process.

The Benson program provided books, writing exercises, audio CDs, and in-person classes. As part of the writing exercises, I began journaling every day. Through journaling, I looked into the closest relationships in my family and saw, for the first time, that there were several dramatic concerns and issues and past events that I needed to address head-on. I mustered up the courage and worked on forgiving myself and others in my life. I had been sexually abused by an older relative in my younger years. So I gained enough courage to confront him in college. And he apologized. But I had never really forgiven him. I took on really letting go of the energy I was using to be angry at others who had caused me harm and using that energy for something much healthier, more worthwhile. I took on using that energy to initiate and carry through forgiveness. It was a truly profound decision—one that I never have second thoughts about. I consider our relationship mended. In fact, our relationship has blossomed since. And we have become very close.

I also saw my deceased parents in a new light, looking at my father's emotional outbursts with compassion instead of resentment. I began to understand that he had been abused by his father as a child, those memories influencing his own actions towards our family, and he had lacked the tools, clarity or understanding that I had in coping with abuse. I was able to cope with lashing out at others and, eventually, was able to heal.

Then there was my relationship with Mom. For so long, I had been a bit angry with Mom for not being able to stand up to Dad. Then through journaling, I began to see my mother's inability to stand up for herself in a new light. I began to see her lack of courage as a reflection of the environment she grew up in, where men dictated and dominated the culture. It wasn't until after my mom had Mary that attitudes towards women began to shift slightly. Mary grew up in the era of the women's liberation movement. That was when women's rights were just starting to become recognized. So I can understand why Mary felt so much resentment towards Mom. She had ridden the wave of women's rights. Mom, on the other hand, was raised at a time when it was okay to treat women unfairly, a time when it was the norm for women to take mistreatment from men, a time when it was actually discouraged for women to challenge men.

That said, in trying to relate to everyone with whom I had been angry before, I quickly began to bring a level of understanding and compassion to these relationships. Then I started digging myself out of entrenched opinionated positions about family members and friends. And that's when the profound process of healing began.

CHAPTER 9

A Paradigm Shift Into Enchanted Wellness

A profound shift suddenly took place. The leadership course had enabled me to reach a state where I could finally love myself. It was such a profound experience, gaining that sense of knowledge of and love for myself, that for the very first Valentine's Day, I was okay with who I was. I actually loved myself, and even though I was single, I—for the first time—did not despise Valentine's Day. I was alone on the day of the holiday, but I was content with that. Then, I realized that I hadn't been employing the distinctions I had learned from Landmark Forum, which included not only loving myself for who I was but also loving myself for who I was not.

This exceptional and profound shift quickly transgressed, and I started applying the same principles to my health state. So, not only had I acquired a sense of love for myself, but I also learned to love my illness. The shift was so profound that I finally forgave myself for having this illness called multiple sclerosis. Prior to the shift, I was enraged at the fact that I had gotten ill. I was in my thirties. I thought to myself, how could I possibly get this disease? At that age, I thought, I shouldn't have been getting any kind of disease. So, when I came to the realization that I had been angry at MS and angry at myself for getting MS, I experienced another "eureka" moment. And I knew that letting go of the mental stress was vital for my well-being.

I began shifting my focus from fighting the disease, being at odds with the disease, and being angry with the symptoms to embracing and caring for my body and mind and really being present in the moment. So, I loved the disease for what it was, and I loved it for what it was not. In my relentless, personal quest for what I could love about MS, I decided to alter what it stood for. I no longer associated MS with multiple sclerosis. I decided that MS would, from then on, mean maximum strength. I couldn't have realized the profound shift without the attainment of a strong sense of gratitude. Being grateful for MS is what enabled me to accept, love, and embrace who I was and who I wasn't. I became grateful for MS because it had become a tool through which I could attain acute sensory awareness of what was happening in my mind as well as my body.

Through this tool, for example, I could sense when I had accumulated hazardous stress levels and how and when my body was responding to all the stress. Signs sent by my body would then reveal to me that something was wrong. For instance, when running, I would sometimes feel a heat sensation in the middle of my back. Consequently, my mind would know to tell my body to slow down, knowing that overheating causes MS symptoms to intensify. This kind of self-awareness was probably one major reason I never pushed myself as a triathlete; I never pushed for speed at the expense of my health. The illness, therefore, had opened my eyes to all the things that it was teaching me about my own body, my own mind, and my own capacities. This, I started to see as a major blessing. And my sense of gratitude enabled me to realize the profound shift in paradigm.

Like the Landmark Forum, this paradigm shift was another turning point in my life, particularly in my journey to healing. The shift enabled me to re-evaluate my attitude and perspectives towards different aspects of my life. I realized that, prior to the shift, I had invested a significant amount of my energy, focus, and time to being angry and afraid and trying to survive. I consider the shift as a defining moment of self-clarity. Observing my own state of mind around my health allowed me to experience a new freedom. This discovery was so powerful that it went far beyond what any drug could have provided. The entire process of self-realization, however, was a slow one, particularly because letting go and easing away the mental stress generated from my past trauma from mental and sexual abuse, my mother and father dying, and my diagnosis was among the most difficult things I have had to do in my life. It was also a slow process because I had a great deal of forgiveness to do; I had to forgive others, and I had to forgive myself before I could reach the state of loving myself, others, and the disease. It surely was a slow process, but I managed to make it through.

As I progressed with my visualizations, meditative practices, and journaling, I began to see my symptoms decrease more and more. So, I slowly reduced the dosage of the drugs I had been administering to myself with my doctor's permission. Within just three months of starting the meditation and visualization practices, my symptoms had come to a complete halt. An MRI scan revealed that the lesions in my brain had shrunk dramatically. This astonished the doctors, so they placed me in a special study to better understand why I was so successful in reducing, minimizing and vanishing the symptoms that had gripped me for so long. Being completely symptom-free and ecstatic about it, I marched into my bedroom on the night of Father's Day of 2008. I marched in with a range of emotions rushing through me and adrenalin pumping through my body from the thrill and shock of what I was about to do. I marched directly to the medical waste garbage can and threw my package of used syringes that I had been using to administer the MS drugs. Then, with a sigh of relief, I said to myself, "I don't need these anymore!" That was the last time I had placed my hands on those syringes. And never again did I see that MS drug.

Incidentally, earlier that evening, as I administered the last shot, it caused a blood bruise and created a small skin scar. It was the first time that had ever happened in the eight years I had administered shots to myself. Taking that incident as a positive sign, I decided that it was time that my journey with those MS drugs came to an end. Cutting off all drugs was not the easiest decision to make. I felt like I had to replace the "effects" of the drugs with something effective and healthy. So I became interested in the benefits of exercise.

I began to study exercise and fitness more thoroughly and learned crucial and relevant information. I learned that one of the key psychological benefits of regular exercise is an increase in self-esteem. I also learned that one of the key physical benefits of exercise is a decrease in the perception of pain. When you exercise, your body releases chemicals called endorphins. These endorphins interact with the receptors in your brain that reduce your perception of pain. Endorphins also trigger a positive feeling in the body, similar to that of morphine. These same hormones trigger positive feelings in the same way that drugs such as morphine would. Other chemicals released during exercise are known as serotonin and dopamine. Both chemicals are involved in promoting positive feelings and an overall happy mood, the former being linked to mood regulation and the latter being associated with promoting happiness. Those who are used to exercising regularly are surely familiar with that feeling that follows a run or workout, often described as being "euphoric." That feeling, known as a "runner's high," can be accompanied by a positive and energizing outlook on life. Regular exercise has been strongly associated with the following physical and psychological health benefits:

- Significant reduction in stress
- Reduction in anxiety and feelings of depression
- Boost in self-esteem
- Improvement in sleep quality
- Strengthened immune system
- Improved heart health.
- Increase in energy levels
- Lower blood pressure
- Positive mindset
- Improved muscle tone and strength
- Gut health
- Reduction in body fat

Unquestionably, being physically active is vital for every individual's health, but it is even more crucial for individuals with a health condition like MS. From personal experience, I can attest to the miraculous benefits of exercising. Today, I am grateful for having gone to that neurologist. I am grateful that he so frankly told me that I would most likely be disabled within ten years. If that neurologist hadn't said to me what he did, I probably would have gone on with my life casually until I fell severely ill from MS. I probably would not have learned to swim, and I definitely would have never gone on to start or complete any triathlon. I had not ridden my bike for more than ten miles, and I probably never would have if I hadn't heard those words. That doctor's words had left me upset but determined and motivated. So I jumped at every single opportunity that presented itself, from hiking and skiing to swimming, running, and biking. Because I jumped at every opportunity, my fitness level became better than it had ever been. As a consequence of my extreme fitness, I became healthier than anyone would ever imagine an MS patient to be.

Once my triathlon and mountain climbing career surpassed their peak, my recurring injuries forced me to start looking into something different. As per my chiropractor's recommendations, I started practicing yoga three times a week as a means of healing the plantar fasciitis that made it nearly impossible for me to run without any pain. My chiropractor also recommended yoga for strengthening my body's nervous system, which is critical for healing any autoimmune disease. Although I had initially underestimated the effects of yoga, I soon discovered how powerful it truly is. I discovered that by doing yoga, you could release toxins from your body in almost no way that anything else can help you release it. After several months of yoga, I had radically cleansed my mind and my body. And, as an added advantage, my foot healed.

Moving my body was, in fact, a form of stress reduction. A good yoga, cardio run or swim was always effective in giving me a boost of energizing for the day and making me feel fresh and renewed. Not only did exercising make me feel great, but it also kept my waistline under control. Being sick with MS or any other autoimmune condition can make it extremely difficult to sustain the motivation to move. When I was experiencing symptoms of MS and I was experiencing extreme fatigue, I had to mentally force myself to go for a swim or a run or do strength training. And I always felt just a little better after I exercised.

The hardest part was always getting out the door every day. I did, however, have incentives. I had my masters swimming group to rely on, my triathlete buddies to run and cycle with, and friends to practice strength training with at times. Buddies make the biggest difference in getting out the door and helping with consistency.

Accordingly, with this new paradigm, I discovered the power of thoughts—the same powers portrayed in the movie *The Secret*. Like the movie, mind-body medicine placed emphasis on the Law of Attraction, which essentially postulates that an individual's thoughts, feelings, and or desires pave the way for the manifestation of particular outcomes or events. Positive thoughts attract positive experiences, and negative thoughts attract negative experiences. Yet all thoughts can only be manifested through an individual's actions because believing in and focusing on the desired outcome hard enough is likely to lead to a commitment to making it happen. In the long run, such desired outcomes can be attributed to those persisting thoughts and desires.

While watching "The Secret," I instantly recalled the story of the woman in the movie who had breast cancer. Western medicine and treatments were not yielding any improvements, so she decided to take a different course of action. She continuously fed herself positive affirmations, and she constantly assured herself that she would be healed. This empowering internal discourse drove her to truly believe that she would be healed. Then the unimaginable happened. She actually healed from breast cancer. Her positivity and her powerful thoughts attracted her desired outcome.

Another extremely powerful and inspirational story was of a man who had been completely paralyzed from an airplane crash. Lying in bed all day, every day, with nearly all the bones in his body broken, he didn't have much to turn to except his own thoughts. Despite having been told by all his doctors that he would be paralyzed for life, he nurtured a positive mindset and set some pretty ambitious goals for himself. He vowed that he would walk out of the hospital by that coming Christmas, which was six months. Every single day, he visualized how he would walk out of that hospital, and he did. He started walking by the six-month deadline and was home by Christmas.

Mind-body medicine is based on the same principles: the power of visualization and the power of one's own thoughts, the power of positivity and the law of attraction. Today, even Western physicians and researchers have recognized the legitimacy and effectiveness of mind-body healing because of the extensive evidence available. The mind-body course addressed in detail how an individual's thinking impacts their body, narrowing the lens on stress. Taking part in the course and learning all the details of the power of thought, I became conscious of how terrible my thoughts tended to be. Life felt like an accident waiting to happen. I was nearly always pondering something negative or even catastrophic taking place. When driving, I often thought about the possibility of crashing with my car. And more similar thoughts crossed my mind on a regular basis. Having MS and knowing that your bodily functions could start numbing up or shutting down at any time is an alarming feeling. You feel a constant state of anxiety as you realize how fragile everything in life is. You have to be on guard every waking minute. But you only need to slip up once. And that's how far away I felt from catastrophe, just one small mistake

This, in mind-body medicine, was termed catastrophe-thinking, thinking of the worst possible outcomes taking place, which is exactly what I did prior to practicing mind-body medicine. Taking those courses, however, opened my eyes to all the different modes of thought an individual can adopt and how each mode can impact stress levels, which consequently impact the body. So from those mind-body courses, I learned a great deal about different healing modalities, all of which focused on filling one's thoughts and mind with positivity.

The courses, coupled with flashbacks of scenes from *The Secret*, were not only a source of inspiration and enlightenment, but they also granted me validation and the thought that perhaps my future wasn't so helpless after all. I quickly shifted my way of thinking, "If cancer patients could make tumors the size of baseballs disappear, I can make my illness disappear." So I set my mind on making myself heal, and I set myself a three-month timeline, which was my next MRI appointment.

Another eye-opening film was the documentary What the Bleep Do We Know!? Unlike The Secret, which is based more or less on a set of philosophical thoughts and beliefs, this documentary was based on principles of neuroscience and quantum physics, much of which has been proven to be scientifically sound. What was profound and striking for me were the visuals of the female character's experiences with negativity. As the documentary's main focus processed negative thoughts, visuals of the inside of her body were shown, unveiling the remarkable effects of one's own thoughts. The film portrayed the range of reactions and changes that the body undergoes as a result of different thought processes. While the film may be considered by some as a pseudoscience, I consider much of what it has covered to be a reflection of real, powerful mechanisms. The recollections depicted in that film helped to validate much of what I had learned with Landmark.

Then there was the neuroscientist Joe Dispenza, whose powerful story offered inspiration and validation. Like me, he was a triathlete. Once in the middle of a triathlon, as he was making a turn with his bike, he got hit by a truck. The truck had smashed right into his back and broke several vertebrae, leaving his spine completely shattered.

He wasn't supposed to heal or walk again. His only chance for a normal life was if he had back surgery. Dispenza was not ready to accept. He left the hospital with his mind set on healing himself and walking again—without surgery and without any of the drawbacks of Western medicine. In just over nine weeks, Dispenza was walking on his feet again, fully recovered, and about three months after the incident, he was back to training. Today, he is a world-renowned figure in the field of mind-body medicine, telling his story, inspiring others, and becoming successful in the process.

After his remarkable experience, Dispenza made it his mission to validate the miraculous power of the mind. So he took up neuroscience, which has validated, through numerous studies, the power of the mind and the mind-body connection.

Such stories of success with mind-body medicine were pivotal in my pursuit of some kind of reassurance. They were critical in helping me put everything into perspective and for serving as a source of inspiration for me to continue in my pursuit.

CHAPTER 10

Love Heals

*A*fter forgiving my relatives for the damage inflicted upon me, I took it upon myself to stop hating men. I had a pathological hatred of men brought about by a lifetime of being abused by them. The best I could do for myself to avoid being hurt by them was to stay as far away from them as I possibly could, but my success record there wasn't exactly 100%. After doing a great deal of work on myself, from forgiving and accepting of others to attaining a state of self-realization, gratitude, and self-acceptance, I finally met my soulmate, a unison that was so strong we became engaged only a year after dating.

Dan and I met on a bike tour, raising funds for MS on Martha's Vineyard in the spring of 2005 through a mutual friend, Martha. He was immediately taken by my smile, my big brown eyes, and my hearty laugh. As for me, I liked the fact that Dan had been an athlete, of course, along with many other things. He had been a long-distance runner since junior high school and competed in cross country running through college. He even ran the Boston Marathon three times in the 1980s.

After a few months of dating, we moved in together to Boston. I was diagnosed with MS in 2000, and by 2006, when we got married, I was self-administering a daily shot of a drug designed to slow down the immune system. One of the biggest fears about MS is what it can do for your relationship prospects. Because while there's a limit in what you can do, as you go through the dating phase, you realize that there is a limit in what a partner will put up with. You worry that if people think they are going to be signing up for the dual role of boyfriend and caretaker, then they will run away. But Dan was nothing like that.

Although we first met five years after my diagnosis and I had been experiencing a considerable amount of MS symptoms, he did not show any signs of fear or aversion. He was, however, aware of my diagnosis. On our first date, he finished cooking a dinner I had started because I was so fatigued to finish cooking it myself. I lay down and fell asleep, and then he woke me up for a wonderful dinner. After dinner, I was still exhausted, so I thought coffee might help. We decided to walk to the local Starbucks; I knew I could manage to walk there because it was only about a football field away. Going into the store, Dan behind me, I tripped on the steps and fell. As he leaned down to help pick me up, I was so embarrassed that I jumped up hurriedly. This only made matters worse because my head clashed right onto his teeth, which made him fall down. This incident, which I had thought was embarrassing, actually didn't affect Dan, and neither did my lack of ability to finish cooking dinner. Instead, we started laughing hysterically at each other.

I knew then that I was in safe hands, ones that would care for me and make me feel loved for who I am. I knew that, with Dan, I would feel comfortable in my own skin and forget that I had something called an illness.

Once we got engaged, we started living together. Ever since, Dan has become my confidant, my hero, and my support system. And I have become his confidant, his hero, and his support system. He provides me with my daily dosage of oxytocin, and I provide him with his. This chemical, released by my brain every time Dan hugs me, helps me relieve stress and makes me feel just downright amazing. When he gives me my daily hug, my body indulges in that incredible feel-good high, which affects my mood for the rest of the day. We have had a loving partnership with daily hugs, kisses, and other forms of romance. Since the day I met Dan, I have been grateful that I had transformed myself and that I had broken free from a vicious cycle of attracting only jerks. Having a husband and a partner that treats you like a queen and friend is priceless, not to mention that he has been a major contributor to my healing journey. That said, a great spouse, friend, partner, or family member can be a great support system for anyone's healing journey, as was my husband throughout mine.

CHAPTER 11

Gift Of Jordan

My partner Dan attended Deerfield Academy from 1977 to 1980. One day, in 2005, he was invited to his 25-year class reunion. Coincidentally, one of his classmates happened to be the current king of Jordan, King Abdullah. The then-prince was so inspired by his own experience in attending Deerfield Academy that he decided to build a private co-educational Academy in the Middle East, the first of its kind, called King's Academy. During their 25-year class reunion, the king invited the entire class of 1980 to visit the country. Luckily, Dan was able to go, and even more, luckily, I was actually able to go with him even though we were just dating at the time. Of course, I was excited about the opportunity, so I accepted the offer.

The entire trip was an all-expense-paid trip from New York City to Jordan.

The entire trip was beyond remarkable. We visited Roman ruins, visited little Petra, an incredible archaeological site in the desert, stayed at five-star hotels, floated in the Dead Sea, rode in Jeeps across the Wadi Rum desert, and rode on camels. We visited the site of the King's Academy, which was nearing completion. And, on our last evening, the hosts actually rolled out the red carpet for us in the middle of the Wadi Rum while playing the theme music to Lawrence of Arabia. They ended the night with some amazing fireworks.

That evening, the king actually thanked us for coming. He invited us and paid for our entire trip, and then he thanked us. Unbelievable.

He wasn't what many people would think of when thinking of a king. He was extremely kind, humble, and hospitable. And he even said that if we had any friends who wanted to come to Jordan, he would be honored to have them come as his guests.

While visiting King's Academy, we met the Turkish architects and engineers responsible for designing King's Academy. They were extremely friendly and recommended us to visit Istanbul, raving about the beauty of the city and how we would love it there. When hearing these engineers and architects talk about Istanbul, I remembered a friend of mine who worked as a Harvard professor telling me that the most interesting place he had ever been to was Istanbul, Turkey. Dan and I decided we would go to Istanbul one day, perhaps on our honeymoon (that we delayed until we had the time and finances to do).

Jordan had a profound impact on us. The capital city of Amman was amazing. The King's assistant and his staff were wonderful people. They made us feel like we were in a magical Wonderland because we were treated by the king and everything was on the king's behalf. All the cities we visited were incredible; Wadi Rum, the Dead Sea, the desert, the city of Petra, and the Gulf of Aqaba: every place was just so beautiful, to say the least. I even had an opportunity to practice swimming for a triathlon in the Gulf of Aqaba. Although the water was salty, I enjoyed every minute of swimming in it. It didn't matter to me if it was salty; I needed to swim to continue my training.

So, the people in Jordan were wonderful, and we took the advice of the Turkish engineers and traveled to Istanbul three years later.

CHAPTER 12

Istanbul

The people in Istanbul were wonderful. The most interesting—and funny—thing was the carpet sellers who ran after people trying to get them to buy carpets. The call to prayers, I would say, was most profound. The call to prayer (**adhan**) is delivered five times a day by a muadhan to remind Muslims to come to mandatory prayer and leave worldly matters behind. That chanting enhanced and deepened a spiritual experience within ourselves in both Jordan and Istanbul. Our experience in Istanbul was much more profound in terms of gaining a heightened state of spirituality, perhaps because we were staying near the Hagia Sophia and the Blue Mosque. Those calls to prayer and the chanting started at the break of dawn. At each call for prayer, crowds of men and women alike would halt whatever they were doing to rush to the mosques for their prayers. Being amongst them and witnessing such a scene multiple times a day was surprising and moving. Their level of commitment to practicing their rituals, their level of reverence for their beliefs was mesmerizing. We were allowed to enter the Blue Mosque in Istanbul, so we listened and watched up close. We were transfixed.

In witnessing such an incredible manifestation of spirituality, my husband and I were so greatly impacted that we decided to improve our own meditative practices. After I had shrunk my brain lesions back home, I had let go of my meditative practices. But witnessing those profound prayers in Istanbul and Jordan reignited the initial sense of purpose I had acquired for myself when taking those mind-body courses. I realized my commitment had been strong only through times of despair but dwindled as my health improved. Prior to Jordan and Turkey, my meditation was inconsistent. Seeing the level of commitment among nearly every person in those two countries was a reminder. It was a reminder of how meditation, positivity, and spirituality are a lifestyle, a way of living and not merely a temporary treatment method for our ailments. Muslims do not opt to pray only when they are sick or when they are going through rough times. They pray every single day, five times a day, for their entire lives.

Overall, our stay in Istanbul was a worthwhile experience. The people were amazing and beautiful. It was powerful to witness the amalgamation of different beliefs, both Muslims and non-Muslims living together peacefully. The food was incredible. The taste of that simple yet elegant and delicious breakfast, the black tea, olives, tomatoes, bread and the delicious cheese are still vivid. Prior to our shift to veganism, Turkish food was by far our favorite. It was so full of many wonderful flavors, nothing like what we are used to in the US. Surprisingly, we eventually got used to the 5 am call to prayer.

CHAPTER 13

From Meat And Potatoes To A Daily Kale Smoothie

My dietary habits were far from aspirational growing up in Iowa. My typical meals centered on meat and potatoes, from pigs in a blanket to meatloaf and more. Being a farm family and raising livestock made a meat-based diet even more convenient for us. Of course, we were unaware of the negative health effects of these eating habits, as were most others. Our poor diet ensued for years. Over time, my diet improved.

I began looking beyond our farm diet when we went on vacation as a family. My parents didn't have much of an adventurous diet, so we rarely got to try new food. One reason we enjoyed vacations so much was that it allowed us to be adventurous foodwise. For example, when we visited my relatives in California, we ate at these unique ethnic restaurants, where we tried delicious dishes that were beyond our typical bland meat-potato diet. Another significant contributor to my gradual shift away from my Iowan diet was my older sister, Mary. She had always been a bit of an exception at our house because she was quite a foodie. And she loved exploring all kinds of cuisine. She was one of the reasons I began opening my mind to trying new food. I remember visiting her and her husband with my parents at a young age and how she always cooked interesting gourmet food such as carrot ginger soup or marinated lamb. At such a young age, I remember looking at her food and shuddering with disgust, mainly because I had come to expect meat and potatoes. Once I knew better, though, I was able to recognize the true value of what she had been cooking. Mary helped me become more adventurous with my food, and I went from being disgusted by her non-potato-meat diet to embracing it and viewing it as something unique, different, and valuable. Today, I'm grateful that she exposed me to that new realm of eating.

But it wasn't until I moved to Chicago that I truly had the opportunity to taste an incredible variety of foods. Chicago was a hub for numerous ethnicities and cultures, so anyone who wanted to try new food had an array of restaurants to choose from. There were Thai restaurants, Korean restaurants, Chinese and Indian restaurants, and many more ethnic variations of cuisine. Living in Chicago allowed me to become more diverse in what I ate and how I ate. Yet, my diet was still considerably unhealthy.

Although I gradually grew out of my childhood eating habits, I still hadn't figured out what constituted healthy eating—until the spring of 2008. During that spring, I participated in an eye-opening extreme health conference, which became a major turning point in my life. The conference was a source of inspiration for me.

For the first time, I gained considerable insight into a range of dietary habits. Some presenters spoke about raw food. Others spoke about Ayurvedic medicine, which ironically advocates the consumption of cooked food, unlike raw food diets. And then there were vegans who keenly promoted the health benefits of veganism. Being avid athletes, Dan and I went into that conference with the intention of simply attending and perhaps acquiring some information on how to feed our bodies in a way that would complement our athletic lifestyle. We went in there with slight curiosity, and we walked out with an open mind.

Thanks to that conference, I came to the realization that I needed to make a radical shift in what and how I ate if I wanted to sustain a healthy mind and body. And Dan was right on board with me. We knew we needed to change in order to improve our health, but we were unsure of what to do and how or where to start.

Although I was initially confused and overwhelmed, being a tri-athlete later paved the way for a smooth transition from the meat and potato-based diet to a much healthier one. Passing by a Borders book-store one day—when bookstores once flourished across all towns—I came across a book that attracted my attention: the title was *Thrive – A Plant-Based Eating Guide for Athletic Performance.* The author, Brendan Brazier, was a professional triathlete. And having found his book at a time when I was at the peak of my triathlon career, I instantly took an interest in what he had to say.

By using a striking analogy, Brazier explained what eating the right food meant for him. He explained how caring for his body improved his performance significantly, comparing his performance pre-to-post veganism to driving a Mercedes race car versus a Chevy. What was his secret weapon? Veganism. He chose to stick to the diet because it enhanced his performance and gave him an edge over other triathletes, enabling him to win more races.

His book addressed individuals like myself who were new to vegan-ism. He recommended that we start by eating a salad for lunch every day and gradually develop a more consistent and purely vegan diet. I took to heart this advice, as did Dan, who was a long-distance runner interested in enhancing his own performance. A radical shift in our eat-ing habits was initially difficult to sustain, so Dan and I took a while to adapt to our new meals. The farm girl in me resisted jettisoning meat, but I continued educating myself about plant-based diets, our current factory farming methods, and how horrible they are.

Gradually, we were able to eat a salad for lunch every day, slowly eliminating various meats and replacing them with more vegetables. We eliminated red meat from our diet, then pork, chicken and fish, and within a few years, we became full vegetarians. Once we became vegetarians, our diet sort of fossilized for quite a while, mainly because of how difficult it was to give up dairy, eggs, and several other foods. When we finally made the full shift to veganism, we became 70% raw foodists.

While Brendan's story was inspiring, I also had something else in mind in opting for a vegan diet. At the time, I had already significantly shrunk the lesions in my brain, and my symptoms essentially disappeared, but I was still taking the MS drug. I knew I needed to change that. After being introduced to veganism and reading Brendan's advice, I experienced flashbacks of talks within my MS support group. I recalled many of the women and young girls in the group saw significant improvements in MS symptoms when shifting their diet to vegetarianism. Adopting vegetarianism means cutting off meat and most other inflammatory foods, which means that less inflammation occurs in the body. In the case of MS patients, less inflammation denotes a reduction in MS symptoms. Having already reduced my brain lesions and have improved my health state, I strongly felt that all I needed to do to free myself of the drug was adopt a less inflammatory diet.

As it turns out, the lack of inflammation is another reason many professional athletes have turned to vegetarian diets. Not only does a vegetarian diet guarantee less inflammation, but digesting vegetarian food also consumes less energy, which leaves more energy for exercise and other activities. Anyone with MS can confirm that the thought of gaining more energy is good, and I was no exception. The thought of gaining more energy heightened my interest in veganism even more. With more energy, I thought, I could finally stop taking the drug. With less inflammation and more energy, I thought, I could finally live drug-free and symptom-free. Plus, I was beyond exhausted both mentally and physically from shooting myself with needles several times a week. All the signs were there, so I decided to take the leap. I was resolute in my decision, and Dan was right there by my side every step of the way.

Without Dan, I doubt that I would have successfully altered my diet. Such a change doesn't involve merely replacing one dish or ingredient with another or trying out a new diet temporarily until one heals from an illness. Rather, it is a permanent lifestyle change. Such a radical shift comes with a complete change in mindset and a shift in cultural norms and values. Altering my farm-nurtured mindset where I valued the meat and potato diet to a mindset that embraced purely vegetable-based meals triggered a sort of culture shock. This phase, however, was quite pivotal, and I considered it as a sign of a successful transition.

By the time I surpassed the vegetarian phase and became a full-time vegan, I had noticed many positive changes in my body. I felt like my body had been granted a new lease on life. I saw an incredible boost in my energy levels. I no longer experienced insomnia, especially after cutting out coffee, and my stomach issues disappeared. Most importantly, MS had disappeared. The lesions in my brain had shrunk even more, and I no longer experienced MS symptoms. Having been on MS drugs for almost a decade, finally becoming symptom-free marked a major turning point in my lifelong battle with MS. This was the point when I became most grateful for having changed my diet. By being drug-free, my body was finally free of those dreadful side effects, which could be as unbearable as the MS symptoms themselves. In making my lesions disappear and being symptom-free, I was able to finally stop pricking myself with those horrendous MS needles nearly every day. I had shot so many needles that I became practically addicted to them like a cocaine addict.

I had been miserable on the MS medications. After my body developed antibodies to the first drug, I started taking another drug that triggered some dreadful side effects. The flu-like symptoms, the skin breakouts, and several other side effects had worsened so much that my doctor decided to reduce my dosage. My body sometimes exploded with hives, and I was barely able to go to work. Initially, I had been so clueless about the source of the skin breakouts that I paid a visit to the dermatologist, who assured me that my breakouts were not so much a topical issue as a psychological issue. Since I hadn't made any significant changes in my lifestyle that could have triggered the breakouts, he explained that the cause was likely a result of excessive stress. When he asked me what was going on in my life at the time, I was taken by surprise. I had never been asked by a traditional Western medicine practitioner what I had going on in my life. What did my life have to do with my skin breakouts? Everything. The dermatologist explained how breaking out was my body's response to excessive stress.

Once I inquired about whether the breakouts could have been a side-effect of the medication, he explained that the medication could have been partly responsible. He, however, insisted that my emotional state was the main culprit. The biggest sources of stress in my life at the time were my job, my MS diagnosis, and shooting myself with needles on a daily basis.

The emotional turmoil from my job came from my boss's constant bickering and yelling for almost no reason. Even after confronting her, which would resolve our issues temporarily, she would almost instantly start yelling for no reason again. I hated my job because of her. I also experienced a great deal of emotional turmoil from the shots. Injecting myself with that strong and unpleasant medicine every day was anything but fun. Not only was it physically draining, but it was emotionally exhausting.

During this time, I tried many different types of healing. I went to an Indian shaman who spit alcohol on me and blew smoke on my face. That didn't work. I tried Reiki, acupuncture, and Rolfing shiatsu. Those weren't so successful either. Admittedly, acupuncture did help relieve my symptoms a bit. The problem, though, was that I became practically addicted to acupuncture. I had to go every single weekend, which was as soon as the effect of acupuncture wore off and the extreme dizziness and other symptoms crept up again.

When the doctor boldly suggested that I should quit my job to attain peace of mind and find relief, I was stunned. I was amazed at how certain he was of the mind-body connection and how he instantly attributed my physical symptoms to a purely psychological mechanism. I eventually quit my job. And the dermatologist was right. My psychological state of agitation had accumulated. And my body managed the stress with breakouts. Once I quit my job and reduced the number of shots I had been taking, I managed to reduce my stress levels significantly. Once my stress levels dipped, my breakouts and all other skin issues disappeared. The greatest insight gained from this experience was the discovery that stress has the tendency to knock the body's equilibrium off balance, triggering symptoms.

Through my transitioning process to veganism, I learned many things about the human body. For starters, I learned the importance of feeding the gut microbiome. This is the collection of all microbes living in the intestines, which include bacteria, viruses, and fungi. I learned that having a gut microbiome with a healthy balance of microbes significantly improves human health. A healthy microbiome supports digestion, improves metabolism, promotes a stronger immune system, and more. Most importantly, the gut microbiome plays a significant role in MS due to its effects on the immune system and the brain. Shifting to veganism is one of the best decisions I've ever made.

Today, I consider myself a vegan. I do have a kale smoothie almost every day, but I've learned to add a greater variety of greens to my diet. As a rule of thumb, I try to eat a variety of twenty-six vegetables, fruits, nuts, and seeds. Although I almost never reach my target twenty-six, I try as best I can. Twenty is my norm. So instead of a kale smoothie every day, I may have spinach one day and collard greens or romaine lettuce the next day before eating kale again. I also vary fruits as much as I can and add nuts and seeds to my diet. Most of our meals are raw, with the exception of dinner because Dan and I just couldn't deprive ourselves of cooking dinner together.

Although I do consider myself vegan, I fit under the slightly more lenient category of vegans. This does not merely involve cutting out meat or substituting it with a similar alternative. The main emphasis of a vegetable-based diet should be placed on the consumption of vegetables rather than simply lack of consumption of meats. This is where many people fall short when trying to incorporate a vegan or vegetarian diet into their lives. Instead of basing their meals on raw vegetables, they mimic meat-based diets where they hardly eat any greens. Some eat what's called a vegan junk food diet where they rely on cooked meals, junk food, fake gluten-free bread, and fake meats to compensate for their old diet, depriving themselves of the raw veggies that make up the core of vegetarianism. They claim to be practicing a healthy vegetable-based diet, but they are consuming foods that merely wreak havoc on their gut.

Promoting gut health is vital for people with MS or any other autoimmune disease since the gut is critical for healing. On the other hand, consuming an insufficient amount of greens, whether cooked or raw and lacking a variety in vegetable intake will likely cause an imbalance in your gut microbiome. Consequently, individuals with such an imbalance are at a higher risk of several health issues, including inflammation. For this reason, adopting a vegetable-based diet is one of the most vital factors for healing from MS or any other autoimmune disease. Looking back at my healing journey, I now consider my shift to nutrient-rich foods as one of the primary reasons for my success in healing from MS, of course, alongside my change in mindset and my consistent physical training.

At the start of our transition, Dan and I were a bit nervous about it and how we would be able to persist. However, the vegan diet turned out to be more interesting, unique, and flavorful than our old meat and potatoes diet. Being on a diet turned out to be more exciting and adventurous than we had expected. Most importantly, though, the diet serves my body, and whatever serves my body serves my health and my purpose in life. That's why I went from a meat and potatoes kind of diet to a daily kale smoothie; It feeds my athletic lifestyle.

CHAPTER 14

Drug-Free, Ms Free, Public Speaker

My healing journey through mind-body medicine, lifestyle medicine, diet, exercise and being drug-free is a daily process. Do I ever think that my MS will return? No, it is now in benign status. I've become completely MS-free, yet my healing journey continues. I consider myself in a continuous process of healing, not from MS but from all physical, emotional, or mental imbalances that may creep up into my life. I have been living unremittingly with the same mindset with which I began my journey—the same mindset I had learned through Landmark Education. Maintaining this healing state of mind keeps me in a positive lifestyle that has become my medicine.

Lifestyle medicine is called lifestyle medicine for a reason. Exercising is part of lifestyle, and so are dietary habits. I've learned that such factors that contribute to my lifestyle significantly affect my health. Notably, I've seen and experienced first-hand the benefits of eating a nutrient-dense diet for my health, to the point where skipping salads for a week can have detrimental effects on my gut. In the same way, the positive health-promoting mindset is a constant, almost unconscious state for me, and exercise, meditation and deep breathing on a regular basis are essential ingredients to my lifestyle and health.

Unfortunately, what seems to intimidate many people out of adopting a healthy lifestyle is the false image of perfection people expect of themselves. A positive lifestyle isn't synonymous with perfection. I have learned to strive not for perfection but for improvement. And with flaws and mistakes comes self-discovery. Each step, each mistake, and each relapse for me is a new opportunity to learn, to discover, and to become more aware of myself and the relationship between my mind and body. Each mistake is a chance for self-development, a chance to flourish.

My imperfections have been an unconventional education regarding my body. I've come to learn how trauma and stress are nearly always at the heart of a physical breakdown. Most importantly, I've come to learn how past trauma can seriously hinder any attempts at living a healthy and happy life, sometimes even at a subconscious level. I've learned that stress can come from not only traumatic events but also lifestyle in general, nutrition, and the environment. And I've learned how to manage such stress through a number of modalities, from meditation to exercise. Sometimes doing something as simple as a certain yoga move helps me release a great deal of stress, which leaves me feeling happier and more energized.

Through my healing journey, I've come to love myself. I learned to forgive myself for having the illness, and I learned to love myself for my diagnosis and my imperfections. Then, I forgave and embraced those who had caused me trauma, eventually surpassing the point of mere acceptance and loving them again. Along this journey, I've learned the power of forgiving others as well as myself. Lamenting over what others had done to me and how unfortunate I was only caused me more suffering, trauma, stress, and pain in the long run. Once I was finally able to forgive and love, my healing efforts became more profound and more successful. I learned that enchanted wellness comes from *loving yourself first* and taking on powerful daily practices to relieve stress. For me, a combination of meditation, visualization, exercise, yoga, strength training, running, cycling and swimming always kept me on my feet and enabled me to live stress-free and eventually MS-free.

Finally, through my healing journey, I have learned about the true power of mindset. Regardless of how many measures I could have taken to recover from the illness, I truly believe that I wouldn't have succeeded without the right mindset. If I had still believed that I'd be sick, then I would have remained sick. Believing that I was healthy, even when I was not, however, helped me overcome my illness. I consider my mindset as the foundation for my recovery. Thanks to the right mindset, today, I am living drug-free and MS-free. I shrunk my lesions over a decade ago, and my neurologist confirmed several times that I am 100% MS-free and finally gave me the benign status validating this.

In becoming MS-free and drug-free, I achieved what some may consider the impossible. With millions of people diagnosed with MS— about 40% of whom are either bedridden or require assistance walking— I felt a burning desire to share my story. I hope my journey can inspire others to take the same steps to recovery that I have. That overpowering eagerness to share my journey has led me to pursue public speaking. To accomplish my aim, however, I had one major hurdle to surpass: my fear of public speaking.

It started as a result of a childhood incident. I was in sixth grade giving a speech when, halfway through, I experienced a mental block. I had completely forgotten the rest of the memorized speech. Out of fear and embarrassment, I just froze on stage and cried my eyes out. That was the last time I spoke in public again—until just recently. After an erratic MS journey and a rare recovery, I felt the urge to speak up, to tell my story. With glossophobia, however, I couldn't share much. So, after decades of being unable to speak in public, I felt an overarching urge to conquer my fear.

Taking part in the Landmark forum helped me find my voice and discover that I was the owner of letting my fears get the best of me. Once I realized that I joined the Toastmasters club. The leadership and communication organization is useful for those who need help overcoming communication barriers. Being a natural introvert who had been traumatized at an early age and getting over my fear felt like a mountain climb, but I eventually did it. I've significantly reduced my fear of public speaking, I have to say that I'm definitely not a natural at it, so it's a daily work in progress.

Through Toastmasters, I completed over ten speeches! Then I took on a year of improvisation classes. The year ended with a live show in which my classmates and I stood before a live audience. Most of my classmates were professional actors and comedians looking to advance their communication skills and further their career. I, on the other hand, was there to learn how to get out of my shell. At the show's climax, my classmates showered me with applause. I was proud of myself for having gathered enough courage to even participate in the live show. At this point, I knew that I had taken ownership of my phobia.

After that year, I was invited to speak at conferences, business developmental workshops, and other events. Sometimes, I put together my own workshops and hosted forums where I shared my story before a live audience. Other times, I invited professionals in the field of mind-body medicine to speak at my events. With each event and with each step, I gained more and more confidence as a public speaker— confidence which I put to good use. I took on spreading my story of health and healing to an increasingly larger population. Today, I am still developing myself as a public speaker, and with different mediums such as social media groups, I've been able to share my story and reach out to more people.

Overall, I consider my work as a public speaker as a major accomplishment. I even had a recent TEDx talk about my MS journey, sharing a pivotal story, one that has the potential to benefit other sufferers. Completely recovering from MS or any other disease would be the ideal outcome for anyone hearing my story. I strive to make even the smallest difference in anyone's life, regardless of how trivial it may appear to be. Regardless of whether my story can help someone recover from a disease or simply change their eating habits, I hope that my story can change people's lives for the better.

If anyone were to ask me for a set of practical guidelines for healing from MS, based on my own experience, I would list the following:

+ **Mindset, Mindset, Mindset** - I cannot stress enough the importance of mindset. You have to have the power of the mind because you could eat all the greens in the world and meditate till you're blue in the face. And if you think, "I'm going to be sick!", you will be sick. So that's why I started with the mind. I did create my own program, but it was all intuitive-based and quite random and miraculous at the same time. I am a firm believer in being only what and who you need to be. An individual with MS does not have the disease. Rather, they have the diagnosis, and whether they have the disease or not is their choice. MS stands for "Maximum Strength!"

- **Nutrition** - Proper nutrition is important for living a healthy life in general, but when living with an autoimmune disease such as MS, nutrition is vital. If you could grow your own garden for access to fresh local food or shop at your local farms, that would be the best, as well as eat organic non-GMO foods, especially if you eat animal meat. Eat more plants and real food!

- Eat twenty-six varieties of plants, nuts, seeds and fruits daily to heal and keep a healthy gut microbiome.

- **Exercise** – Long before I started on the path to recovery, exercise was one of the saving graces in my life that gave me focus and gave me a glimpse of the idealized version of myself.

- **Probiotics** - taking probiotics, eating raw and fermented foods. Things that help your gut help your gut heal, and you will heal.

But good health would never be served on a platter, put in a pill or given to you by any doctor. It comes from a growing awareness of one's own body and self and the difference one can truly make from recognizing that awareness and actively feeding it daily.

Simultaneously, it is crucial that every person gets a regular dose of solitude. Getting outside and being in nature is pivotal, not just for a breath of fresh air but also for productivity. Research has even suggested that work productivity improves by up to 45% by being outdoors for thirty minutes. Fresh air has also been shown to have numerous health benefits, from improving digestion, blood pressure levels, mood, and even brain functioning.

So this is the life of an adventure athlete, speaker and author. It seems that I am an anomaly to my former doctor and to everyone else around me. I'm such an anomaly, in fact, that some people still can't believe and won't believe that I have actually healed. Even one of my own brothers will not believe that I have healed, regardless of how hard I try to convince him.

This is my healing journey through Mind Body medicine, lifestyle medicine and exercise. This is my story of how healing is a daily process for me even after having healed from MS. This is my story of a powerful realization, the realization that my MS diagnosis was the greatest gift of my life. It has been the greatest gift of my life because it was a major wake-up call. It raised my own awareness and understanding of myself, my body and my relationships with others. If it weren't for the diagnosis, I would have never forgiven my father or my older relative for the abuse. And if I hadn't done that forgiveness work, I wouldn't have changed my mindset. I wouldn't have met my soulmate and husband. I would not have healed completely from MS.

Now I am living in the context that health is a state of mind. Long-term health comes from within first, then what follows is long-term alterations and sacrifices and a growing awareness of one's own body and self. It comes from recognizing that awareness and feeding it daily. How our life unfolds is predominately our choice. I want to remind you of that small moment just after getting my diagnosis. I received a message in my mind on my first ever meditation practice- that I would receive a diagnosis of multiple sclerosis, and I would heal, and everything would work out. The mind is more powerful than we know. We can treat ourselves, our bodies, like a Mercedes Benz. Or we can live a life of pain, uncertainty, despair, and internal conflict. If we opt for the Mercedes, we ought to fuel it accordingly. We ought to fuel it physically, mentally, emotionally, and spiritually. In the end, the Mercedes will likely take you places you wouldn't expect many other vehicles would take you.

RESOURCES

Every journey is propelled forward by boundless inspirations along the way, and it would be a disservice not to cite the people whose expertise shaped me into the person I am today. So, without further ado, I would like to take the time to acknowledge these incredible people and their publications in the hope that you may benefit from them one day:

HEALING MODELS

Deepak Chopra (The Chopra Center for Wellbeing Journey into Healing Program) - after I healed from MS, I was fascinated by my ability to shrink the lesions in my brain. I became interested in knowing more about healing in general, notably mind-body medicine. So I took this course, and among the most beneficial things I learned about was my body type according to Ayurvedic medicine, the power of my thoughts, meditation and the importance of yoga. We did yoga every morning before the course began and meditation at the beginning of the course each day. I shared my healing journey from MS at the Journey Into Healing conference and afterward. Rudi Tanzi, the co-author of Super Brain, said to me, "When you're ready to publish your book, send me a copy, and I'll help you get published. Please share your story and how you did it with others." That's when I knew that I had something important to share.

Louise Hay - A spiritual friend of mine gave me a workbook written by Louise Hay and said it might help me with MS, so I started reading it and doing the affirmations. Then seeing how great that book was, I started buying all of her books. I then volunteered to do the *I Can Do It* tour while staying at a friend's outside of NYC. She invited multiple speakers, from Wayne Dyer to many other inspiring speakers who shared their stories of overcoming obstacles and/or healing. Louise has adopted the belief that you are responsible for your own disease or condition. She has a resources section for all her ailments, and this is what it says about Multiple Sclerosis (MS): Mental hardness, hard-heartedness, iron will, inflexibility. Fear. The Affirmation to offset this is by choosing loving, joyous thoughts. I create a loving, joyous world. I am safe and free.

Landmark Worldwide - a company, headquartered in San Francisco, which offers personal-development programs. Landmark Education started in 1991 with the licensing of rights to use intellectual property owned by Werner Erhard, who had originated the EST system in the 1970s. www.landmarkworldwide.com

The Wisdom Unlimited Course - takes place over a span of almost a year. Participants work on assigned coursework, exploring aspects of how we relate to our own growth, development and what we can create for ourselves in positive and empowering ways. We then explore the positive impacts we create in the communities in which we live, work, and play. The purpose is to design a life full of love, fun, play and ease. I'm incorporating fun, play and ease into my programs and retreats! Let's make healing fun and playful. www.mindovermind.com/programs

Mind Body Medical Institute by Herbert Benson - In the spring of 2005, when I was experiencing multiple sclerosis (MS), I did Herb Benson's Mind Body program at the Mind Body Medical Institute, now the Benson-Henry Institute at Massachusetts General Hospital (MGH.) I did a twelve-week in-person symptom reduction program that taught us stress-relieving techniques and the most important being meditation. They measured our progress, and by the end, my MS symptoms decreased by 20% in just twelve weeks. Today, I continue to practice what I learned from this course. I am sharing all the tools and techniques I've learned from this program and many others I've done in my book. A great book I would highly recommend is Benson's *Relaxation Response and Beyond the Relaxation Response.* https://bensonhenryinstitute.org/

The Center for Mind-Body Medicine is another nationwide program that offers mind body medicine training programs. This evidence-based, transformational *training* gives you the science and tools you need to make *mind-body medicine* an integral, foundational part of your practice and your life. https://cmbm.org/

Otherwise, you can find a local mind body medicine program near you, mostly through universities or hospitals. Some are covered by insurance. Another option is to research mind-body medicine physicians, mindfulness or meditation practitioners.

The Effect of Diaphragmatic Breathing on Attention, Negative Affect and Stress in Healthy Adults

https://www.ncbi.nlm.nih.gov/pmc/articles/PMC5455070/ provides a scientific overview of the benefits of this type of breathing.

https://www.verywellmind.com/how-to-reduce-stress-by-deep-breathing-2797585 provides a more general overview of the benefits.

I've personally used diaphragmatic breathing to control my defensive reactions towards my family. As a trauma survivor and someone who's experienced mental abuse, this type of breathing allowed me to be more present in my thoughts and control my reactions. It's key to recognize it is a work in progress, and it's helped to significantly calm my mind and behaviors.

SIMILAR HEALING PHILOSOPHIES

The Biology of Belief by Bruce Lipton, Ph.D.

This book explores how cells receive and process information; it shows that genes and DNA do not control our biology. In other words, the cells' environment matters much more than we once thought. Change the cell's environment, and you change the cell's behavior and characteristics. In simpler terms, "Your thoughts affect the cells in your body!" Once I began to monitor and be present to my thoughts and my thinking, the disease started to disappear and eventually went into full recovery.

You Are the Placebo: Making Your Mind Matter by Joe Dispenza, noteworthy for his use of mind-body medicine philosophies plus the law of attraction. I found out about Dr. Dispenza after my healing journey from MS, but his principles are similar to what I teach and believe. He backs up all of his work with science. For more information, visit the link: https://drjoedispenza.com/

Lifestyle Medicine - Lifestyle Medicine is the use of evidence-based lifestyle therapeutic intervention—including a whole-food, plant-predominant eating pattern, regular physical activity, restorative sleep, stress management, avoidance of risky substances, and positive social connection—as a primary modality, delivered by clinicians trained and certified in this specialty, to prevent, treat, and often reverse chronic disease.

For more information, visit the link: https://lifestylemedicine.org/

Thrive Diet - I altered my diet from meat and potatoes to raw food vegan after reading *The Thrive Diet,* a health and fitness book by Brendan Brazier. After successfully shrinking the lesions in my brain using visualization, I wanted to get off the MS drug I was on. I slowly altered my diet and started by eating one big salad per day, and, with the support of my husband, we became raw food vegans. As I shifted my diet to a whole food plant-based diet, my body began to heal more fully, and I got off the MS drug several months later.

For more information: click the link: https://www.brendanbrazier.com/books

Crazy Sexy Cancer and **Crazy Sexy Diet,** book by Kris Carr - Kris's philosophy on her diagnosis was to be happy, eat more greens and drink green juice. This hipster influenced me as she was young like I was and living healthy with chronic cancer. She was my role model for living healthy with a disease, so I took on her lifestyle changes as well and applied them to MS. I even drank a green juice and now drink green smoothie and juice every day! https://kriscarr.com/

Wahls Protocol Diet for MS Treatment: Effectiveness and Foods By Dr. Terry Wahls - After progressive multiple sclerosis landed Dr Wahls in a tilt/recline wheelchair, she exhaustively researched the autoimmune disease and brain biology and embraced the concepts of functional medicine. Determined to overcome her initial dismal diagnosis, she made a choice to rely on food as her medicine and began using paleo concepts as guidelines for her unique, nutrient-rich plan. As her broken biochemistry began to fix itself, Dr Wahls soon retained full mobility and left her wheelchair behind for good. Dr Wahls' transformation was nothing short of miraculous, and she knew these treatments could be life-changing for anyone struggling with an autoimmune condition. Now, Dr Wahls shares her pioneering research along with three levels of nutrient-rich diets that can help you reverse the debilitating symptoms of your disease. The Wahls Protocol gave Dr Wahls her life back. This diet is for meat-based diets only with a commitment of eating 9 cups of vegetables per day, plus organ meats. https://terrywahls.com/

Functional Medicine – gets to your core issue from a diet and lifestyle focus. To find a local Functional Medicine practitioner near you, please see: https://www.ifm.org/

Fiber Fueled

In case you have stomach issues and/or autoimmune Dr. Will's book is great, and his gut rebuilding online program will help you learn how to heal your gut and aid in healing autoimmune conditions! For more information, please see: https://theplantfedgut.com/

GUT-BRAIN ON

A leading-edge voice in neuroscience and GUT-BRAIN integrity, Neurologist Dr. Tom Acklin brings his expertise to people suffering with autoimmune conditions and cancer.

He has worked in Food-as-Medicine/Functional Medicine therapeutics for the last decade, passionate about helping us understand the power of the gut Microbiome in reversing almost everything we call modern disease. Dr. Tom is old fashioned and works one-on-one. Please find his personal contact information at my website: https://www.mindovermind.com/favorite-things

OptimalBody Fitness

The OptimalBody Training Program for MS was born from David Lyons' MS Fitness Challenge charity and his desire to help others who suffer from multiple sclerosis conquer this disease through fitness. His own bodybuilding challenge and his books, David's Goliath and Everyday Health & Fitness with MS are inspirations to others who find trials and obstacles in life and in their fitness challenges too difficult to overcome. David founded and created OptimalBody as a science-based fitness program providing results for people with MS and autoimmune conditions. This program, uniquely designed specifically to overcome limitations has been named the Most Comprehensive MS Fitness Program in the world in both 2021 & 2022. David's 40+ years as a fitness expert and his more than 15 years with MS have made him the recognized leading MS fitness expert worldwide and the only one with MS to be inducted into the National Fitness Hall of Fame.

Personally, as a former triathlete and fitness advocate, I highly recommend this program as it's helped thousands of MS Thrivers improve their health. Strength training and exercise are proven to help the immune system and mood. I know it's helped me with many aspects of life beyond MS as well. For more information, please see https://www.mindovermind.com/favorite-things and/or please us my referral code: https://obpfitness.com?ref=1104

Yoga

As an athlete, yoga has given me access to having a longer endurance athletic life. It has brought me peace and solace in times of need. It also provides a heck of a good workout that stretches, strengthens and lengthens the body. Yoga is considered a moving meditation that prepares you for meditation. I can't be thankful enough for what yoga has added to my life.

A site I thoroughly enjoy and use regularly is **Do Yoga With Me**, an internationally-renown site offering quality yoga instruction, by donation, to users around the world. www.doyogawithme.com. Fiji Mc Alpine is my favorite teacher. ☺

YogaWorks is also a great site that provides paid live online classes nationwide in the U.S. www.yogaworks.com

LifeWave patches offers an affordable stem cell technology which is beneficial for anyone over thirty-five. Personally, I found LifeWave patches a year ago through my neurologist friend Dr. Tom. The patches have helped me reduce the inflammation in my knee so I can now run again! The stem cell patches also help me recover faster from my fitness workouts so I don't feel as sore as I used to. In addition, it's helped me heal my gut, (along with diet changes), improve my sleep and my energy levels are off the charts! I realize eating a plant-based diet helps this as well, but since using these patches, my energy and focus have skyrocketed. I believe in the products so much, I'm now a representative for LifeWave and I'm growing my team and customers. The company culture is amazing and has high integrity. We're a like-minded group of health-conscious team players. If you'd like to find out more about the products, or our team, please see www.mindovermind.com/lifewave and/or contact me at jana@janascholten.com for more information.

USEFUL LINKS

The following resources were provided by Lisa Petrocchi-Merriman, M.A., Psychotherapist

As a Growth Mindset coach, Lisa Merriman works with companies to build sustainable and inclusive cultures by creating an environment of psychological safety. Her unique quality focuses on guiding leaders, mid-level managers and work teams to acquire tools of resiliency and how to communicate, delegate and negotiate with Emotional Intelligence. °°With over ten thousand hours coaching and training diverse individuals and teams, her work has been especially effective for managing workplace and personal distress, giving clients, teams and individuals tools that put them back in charge of their personal and professional lives.

For more information about trauma or Lisa's business coaching and training resources, you can contact her at alignnw@gmail.com or www.oasismind.com

Overview of MS:

https://multiplesclerosisnewstoday.com/multiple-sclerosis-overview

Prevalence of MS in the US:

https://n.neurology.org/content/92/10/e1029

Article on the numbers and effects behind autoimmune diseases:

https://www.gene.com/stories/autoimmune-disease-101

Adverse Childhood Experiences and the effects on children 0-17 yrs of age:

https://www.cdc.gov/violenceprevention/aces/fastfact.html

Types and effects of trauma on autoimmune disease:

https://www.medicalnewstoday.com/articles/trauma

New rational diagnosis for children with complex trauma histories.
https://traumaticstressinstitute.org/wp-
content/files_mf/1276541701VanderKolkDvptTraumaDis.pdf

Abundance of resources including symptoms of trauma, checklists and helpful articles to get people on their way to health and wellbeing.
https://www.thenationalcouncil.org/

Recommended Book's List:

Why People Don't Heal And How They Can by Carolyn Myss, Ph.D.

Perfect Health The Complete Mind Body Guide by Deepak Chopra, M.D.

The Body Keeps The Score by Bessel Van Der Kolk, M.D.

Mind Over Medicine by Lisa Rankin, M.D.

The Spontaneous Healing of Belief by Gregg Braden

The Healing Self by Deepak Chopra, M.D. & Rudolph E. Tanzi, Ph.D.

Super Brain by Deepak Chopra, M.D. & Rudolph E. Tanzi,Ph.D. *Brain Maker* by David Perlmutter, M.D.

Dying to be Me by Arnita Moorjani

Super Attractor by Gabrielle Bernstein

Ask and It is Given by Esther and Jerry Hicks

E-Squared by Pam Grout

Recommended Movies/Documentaries:

The Secret by Rhonda Byrne

Wh at the Bleep do we know and Down the Rabbit Hole

Heal film

Forks Over Knives

The Game Changers

On a final note, I hope that I can share my successful healing with many other people. As I move into the next stage of my life, I intend to help people through the same hurdles that I endured. As such, I'm offering a 10-week Enchanted Wellness program for those diagnosed with MS or autoimmune conditions.

- Would you like to raise your awareness around your life and diagnosis?

- Would you like to be able to generate compassion and forgiveness in your relationships?

- Would you like to create and discover a new future for your health or your life?

- Would you like to improve your communication with others?

If the answer is yes to any of these, my program is an opportunity to fulfill these issues.

Here are the outcomes you can expect from my program:

- Full peace of mind.

- A positive mindset shift.

- Experience a new sense of freedom.

- Have a new relationship with your body.

- See and experience joy.

I invite you to join me in being a healthy thriver! Please visit www.janascholten.com for more information.

Please email me at jana@janascholten.com and let me know which of these actions you will take on! For future programs and events, please visit www.mindovermind.com/programs

ABOUT THE AUTHOR

JANA SCHOLTEN

Jana Scholten of Boston, Massachusetts, was diagnosed with Multiple Sclerosis (MS) in 2001. She suffered for several years with serious MS symptoms. Through various research and programs, Jana discovered that she had a say about her own body and that she did not have to be a victim of the disease. She took on the view that MS was a wakeup call to her to live her life fully. She set about healing relationships in her life, starting with her family and then herself. She shifted how she related to the dis-ease, and began loving MS. She began to listen to her body and what it was telling her. She met her husband-to-be shortly thereafter. As she let go of anger and stress in her life, her symptoms faded to almost nothing. She then took on mind-body medicine, meditation and visualization and shrunk the lesions in her brain. She is now drug and symptom free and in benign status. She is also an endurance athlete.

Jana is committed that others realize their own power in dealing with health challenges by healing through compassion, love and forgiveness. Jana creates programs to empower those with MS and autoimmune disease

To learn more about Her, please visit
www.janascholten.com

Finally, a letter of benign status by my Dr. showing that I am symptom free and MS free since 2008!!

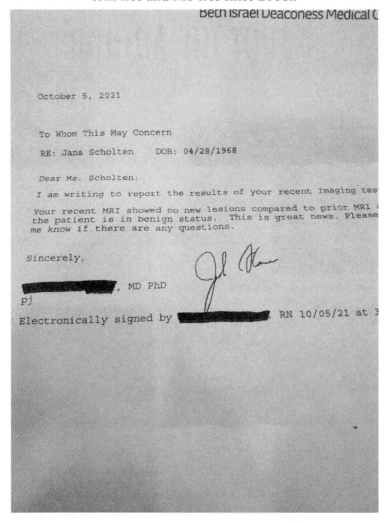

Beth Israel Deaconess Medical C

October 5, 2021

To Whom This May Concern

RE: Jana Scholten   DOB: 04/28/1968

Dear Ms. Scholten:

I am writing to report the results of your recent Imaging tes

Your recent MRI showed no new lesions compared to prior MRI
the patient is in benign status. This is great news. Please
me know if there are any questions.

Sincerely,

███████, MD PhD
pj

Electronically signed by ███████, RN 10/05/21 at 3

A REQUEST

THANK YOU for Reading My Book!

I would love to hear from you. Writing an Amazon review is as easy as answering any of these questions:

* What did you enjoy about the book?

* What is your most valuable takeaway or insight?

* What have you done differently – or what will you do differently – because of what you read?

* To whom would you recommend this book?

Seriously, just two or three sentences would be amazing. Your positive feedback helps to get this book into the hands of those who need it most ☺

I look forward to hearing about the action you took because of this book.

Thank you in advance,

Jana

Download the
Enchanted Wellness Toolkit
(for FREE!)

READ THIS

To help you implement the strategies in this book, I've created several resources, including the *Mindset Hacks and Nutrition Secrets* worksheet. Download them all at no cost whatsoever in the in the *Enchanted Wellness* Toolkit. It's my gift to you. – *Jana Scholten*

Go to www.mindovermind.com/toolkit to get it!

Printed in Great Britain
by Amazon

23149949R00066